S0-ARM-063

Science 700
Teacher's Guide

CONTENTS

Author: **Alpha Omega Publications**

Editor: Alan Christopherson, M.S.

Alpha Omega Publications®

804 N. 2nd Ave. E., Rock Rapids, IA 51246-1759
© MCMXCVI by Alpha Omega Publications, Inc.   All rights reserved.
LIFEPAC is a registered trademark of Alpha Omega Publications, Inc.

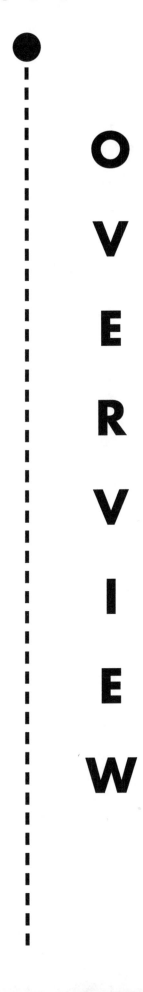

OVERVIEW

SCIENCE

Curriculum Overview
Grades 1–12

Science LIFEPAC Overview

	Grade 1	Grade 2	Grade 3
LIFEPAC 1	YOU LEARN WITH YOUR EYES • Name and group some colors • Name and group some shapes • Name and group some sizes • Help from what you see	THE LIVING AND NONLIVING • What God created • Rock and seed experiment • God-made objects • Man-made objects	YOU GROW AND CHANGE • Air we breathe • Food for the body • Exercise and rest • You are different
LIFEPAC 2	YOU LEARN WITH YOUR EARS • Sounds of nature and people • How sound moves • Sound with your voice • You make music	PLANTS • How are plants alike • Habitats of plants • Growth of plants • What plants need	PLANTS • Plant parts • Plant growth • Seeds and bulbs • Stems and roots
LIFEPAC 3	MORE ABOUT YOUR SENSES • Sense of smell • Sense of taste • Sense of touch • Learning with my senses	ANIMALS • How are animals alike • How are animals different • What animals need • Noah and the ark	ANIMAL GROWTH AND CHANGE • The environment changes • Animals are different • How animals grow • How animals change
LIFEPAC 4	ANIMALS • What animals eat • Animals for food • Animals for work • Pets to care for	YOU • How are people alike • How are you different • Your family • Your health	YOU ARE WHAT YOU EAT • Food helps your body • Junk foods • Food groups • Good health habits
LIFEPAC 5	PLANTS • Big and small plants • Special plants • Plants for food • House plants	PET AND PLANT CARE • Learning about pets • Caring for pets • Learning about plants • Caring for plants	PROPERTIES OF MATTER • Robert Boyle • States of matter • Physical changes • Chemical changes
LIFEPAC 6	GROWING UP HEALTHY • How plants and animals grow • How your body grows • Eating and sleeping • Exercising	YOUR FIVE SENSES • Your eye • You can smell and hear • Your taste • You can feel	SOUNDS AND YOU • Making sounds • Different sounds • How sounds move • How sounds are heard
LIFEPAC 7	GOD'S BEAUTIFUL WORLD • Types of land • Water places • The weather • Seasons	PHYSICAL PROPERTIES • Colors • Shapes • Sizes • How things feel	TIMES AND SEASONS • The earth rotates • The earth revolves • Time changes • Seasons change
LIFEPAC 8	ALL ABOUT ENERGY • God gives energy • We use energy • Ways to make energy • Ways to save energy	OUR NEIGHBORHOOD • Things not living • Things living • Harm to our world • Caring for our world	ROCKS AND THEIR CHANGES • Forming rocks • Changing rocks • Rocks for buildings • Rock collecting
LIFEPAC 9	MACHINES AROUND YOU • Simple levers • Simple wheels • Inclined planes • Using machines	CHANGES IN OUR WORLD • Seasons • Change in plants • God's love never changes • God's Word never changes	HEAT ENERGY • Sources of heat • Heat energy • Moving heat • Benefits and problems of heat
LIFEPAC 10	WONDERFUL WORLD OF SCIENCE • Using your senses • Using your mind • You love yourself • You love the world	LOOKING AT OUR WORLD • Living things • Nonliving things • Caring for our world • Caring for ourselves	PHYSICAL CHANGES • Change in man • Change in plants • Matter and time • Sound and energy

Grade 4	Grade 5	Grade 6	
PLANTS • Plants and living things • Using plants • Parts of plants • The function of plants	CELLS • Cell composition • Plant and animal cells • Life of cells • Growth of cells	PLANT SYSTEMS • Parts of a plant • Systems of photosynthesis • Transport systems • Regulatory systems	LIFEPAC 1
ANIMALS • Animal structures • Animal behavior • Animal instincts • Man protects animals	PLANTS: LIFE CYCLES • Seed producing plants • Spore producing plants • One-celled plants • Classifying plants	ANIMAL SYSTEMS • Digestive system • Excretory system • Skeletal system • Diseases	LIFEPAC 2
MAN'S ENVIRONMENT • Resources • Balance in nature • Communities • Conservation and preservation	ANIMALS: LIFE CYCLES • Invertebrates • Vertebrates • Classifying animals • Relating function and structure	PLANT AND ANIMAL BEHAVIOR • Animal behavior • Plant behavior • Plant-animal interaction • Balance in nature	LIFEPAC 3
MACHINES • Work and energy • Simple machines • Simple machines together • Complex machines	BALANCE IN NATURE • Needs of life • Dependence on others • Prairie life • Stewardship of nature	MOLECULAR GENETICS • Reproduction • Inheritance • DNA and mutations • Mendel's work	LIFEPAC 4
ELECTRICITY AND MAGNETISM • Electric current • Electric circuits • Magnetic materials • Electricity and magnets	TRANSFORMATION OF ENERGY • Work and energy • Heat energy • Chemical energy • Energy sources	CHEMICAL STRUCTURE • Nature of matter • Periodic Table • Diagrams of atoms • Acids and bases	LIFEPAC 5
CHANGES IN MATTER • Properties of water • Properties of matter • Molecules and atoms • Elements	RECORDS IN ROCK: THE FLOOD • The Biblical account • Before the flood • The flood • After the flood	LIGHT AND SOUND • Sound waves • Light waves • The visible spectrum • Colors	LIFEPAC 6
WEATHER • Causes of weather • Forces of weather • Observing weather • Weather instruments	RECORDS IN ROCK: FOSSILS • Fossil types • Fossil location • Identifying fossils • Reading fossils	MOTION AND ITS MEASUREMENT • Definition of force • Rate of doing work • Laws of motion • Change in motion	LIFEPAC 7
THE SOLAR SYSTEM • Our solar system • The big universe • Sun and planets • Stars and space	RECORDS IN ROCK: GEOLOGY • Features of the earth • Rock of the earth • Forces of the earth • Changes in the earth	SPACESHIP EARTH • Shape of the earth • Rotation and revolution • Eclipses • The solar system	LIFEPAC 8
THE PLANET EARTH • The atmosphere • The hydrosphere • The lithosphere • Rotation and revolution	CYCLES IN NATURE • Properties of matter • Changes in matter • Natural cycles • God's order	ASTRONOMY AND THE STARS • History of astronomy • Investigating stars • Major stars • Constellations	LIFEPAC 9
GOD'S CREATION • Earth and solar system • Matter and weather • Using nature • Conservation	LOOK AHEAD • Plant and animal life • Balance in nature • Biblical records • Records of rock	THE EARTH AND THE UNIVERSE • Plant systems • Animal systems • Physics and chemistry • The earth and stars	LIFEPAC 10

	Grade 7	Grade 8	Grade 9
LIFEPAC 1	**WHAT IS SCIENCE** • Tools of a scientist • Methods of a scientist • Work of a scientist • Careers in science	**SCIENCE AND SOCIETY** • Definition of science • History of science • Science today • Science tomorrow	**OUR ATOMIC WORLD** • Structure of matter • Radioactivity • Atomic nuclei • Nuclear energy
LIFEPAC 2	**PERCEIVING THINGS** • History of the metric system • Metric units • Advantages of the metric system • Graphing data	**STRUCTURE OF MATTER I** • Properties of matter • Chemical properties of matter • Atoms and molecules • Elements, compounds, & mixtures	**VOLUME, MASS, AND DENSITY** • Measure of matter • Volume • Mass • Density
LIFEPAC 3	**EARTH IN SPACE I** • Ancient stargazing • Geocentric Theory • Copernicus • Tools of astronomy	**STRUCTURE OF MATTER II** • Changes in matter • Acids • Bases • Salts	**PHYSICAL GEOLOGY** • Earth structures • Weathering and erosion • Sedimentation • Earth movements
LIFEPAC 4	**EARTH IN SPACE II** • Solar energy • Planets of the sun • The moon • Eclipses	**HEALTH AND NUTRITION** • Foods and digestion • Diet • Nutritional diseases • Hygiene	**HISTORICAL GEOLOGY** • Sedimentary rock • Fossils • Crustal changes • Measuring time
LIFEPAC 5	**THE ATMOSPHERE** • Layers of the atmosphere • Solar effects • Natural cycles • Protecting the atmosphere	**ENERGY I** • Kinetic and potential energy • Other forms of energy • Energy conversions • Entropy	**BODY HEALTH I** • Microorganisms • Bacterial infections • Viral infections • Other infections
LIFEPAC 6	**WEATHER** • Elements of weather • Air masses and clouds • Fronts and storms • Weather forecasting	**ENERGY II** • Magnetism • Current and static electricity • Using electricity • Energy sources	**BODY HEALTH II** • Body defense mechanisms • Treating disease • Preventing disease • Community health
LIFEPAC 7	**CLIMATE** • Climate and weather • Worldwide climate • Regional climate • Local climate	**MACHINES I** • Measuring distance • Force • Laws of Newton • Work	**ASTRONOMY** • Extent of the universe • Constellations • Telescopes • Space explorations
LIFEPAC 8	**HUMAN ANATOMY I** • Cell structure and function • Skeletal and muscle systems • Skin • Nervous system	**MACHINES II** • Friction • Levers • Wheels and axles • Inclined planes	**OCEANOGRAPHY** • History of oceanography • Research techniques • Geology of the ocean • Properties of the ocean
LIFEPAC 9	**HUMAN ANATOMY II** • Respiratory system • Circulatory system • Digestive system • Endocrine system	**BALANCE IN NATURE** • Photosynthesis • Food • Natural cycles • Balance in nature	**SCIENCE AND TOMORROW** • The land • Waste and ecology • Industry and energy • New frontiers
LIFEPAC 10	**CAREERS IN SCIENCE** • Scientists at work • Astronomy • Meteorology • Medicine	**SCIENCE AND TECHNOLOGY** • Basic science • Physical science • Life science • Vocations in science	**SCIENTIFIC APPLICATIONS** • Measurement • Practical health • Geology and astronomy • Solving problems

Grade 10	Grade 11	Grade 12	
TAXONOMY • History of taxonomy • Binomial nomenclature • Classification • Taxonomy	**INTRODUCTION TO CHEMISTRY** • Metric units and instrumentation • Observation and hypothesizing • Scientific notation • Careers in chemistry	**KINEMATICS** • Scalars and vectors • Length measurement • Acceleration • Fields and models	LIFEPAC 1
BASIS OF LIFE • Elements and molecules • Properties of compounds • Chemical reactions • Organic compounds	**BASIC CHEMICAL UNITS** • Alchemy • Elements • Compounds • Mixtures	**DYNAMICS** • Newton's Laws of Motion • Gravity • Circular motion • Kepler's Laws of Motion	LIFEPAC 2
MICROBIOLOGY • The microscope • Protozoan • Algae • Microorganisms	**GASES AND MOLES** • Kinetic theory • Gas laws • Combined gas law • Moles	**WORK AND ENERGY** • Mechanical energy • Conservation of energy • Power and efficiency • Heat energy	LIFEPAC 3
CELLS • Cell theories • Examination of the cell • Cell design • Cells in organisms	**ATOMIC MODELS** • Historical models • Modern atomic structure • Periodic Law • Nuclear reactions	**WAVES** • Energy transfers • Reflection and refraction of waves • Diffraction and interference • Sound waves	LIFEPAC 4
PLANTS: GREEN FACTORIES • The plant cell • Anatomy of the plant • Growth and function of plants • Plants and people	**CHEMICAL FORMULAS** • Ionic charges • Electronegativity • Chemical bonds • Molecular shape	**LIGHT** • Speed of light • Mirrors • Lenses • Models of light	LIFEPAC 5
HUMAN ANATOMY AND PHYSIOLOGY • Digestive and excretory system • Respiratory and circulatory system • Skeletal and muscular system • Body control systems	**CHEMICAL REACTIONS** • Detecting reactions • Energy changes • Reaction rates • Equilibriums	**STATIC ELECTRICITY** • Nature of charges • Transfer of charges • Electric fields • Electric potential	LIFEPAC 6
INHERITANCE • Gregor Mendel's experiments • Chromosomes and heredity • Molecular genetics • Human genetics	**EQUILIBRIUM SYSTEMS** • Solutions • Solubility equilibriums • Acid-base equilibriums • Redox equilibriums	**CURRENT ELECTRICITY** • Electromotive force • Electron flow • Resistance • Circuits	LIFEPAC 7
CELL DIVISION & REPRODUCTION • Mitosis and meiosis • Asexual reproduction • Sexual reproduction • Plant reproduction	**HYDROCARBONS** • Organic compounds • Carbon atoms • Carbon bonds • Saturated and unsaturated	**MAGNETISM** • Fields • Forces • Electromagnetism • Electron beams	LIFEPAC 8
ECOLOGY & ENERGY • Ecosystems • Communities and habitats • Pollution • Energy	**CARBON CHEMISTRY** • Saturated and unsaturated • Reaction types • Oxygen groups • Nitrogen groups	**ATOMIC AND NUCLEAR PHYSICS** • Electromagnetic radiation • Quantum theory • Nuclear theory • Nuclear reaction	LIFEPAC 9
APPLICATIONS OF BIOLOGY • Principles of experimentation • Principles of reproduction • Principles of life • Principles of ecology	**ATOMS TO HYDROCARBONS** • Atoms and molecules • Chemical bonding • Chemical systems • Organic chemistry	**KINEMATICS TO NUCLEAR PHYSICS** • Mechanics • Wave motion • Electricity • Modern physics	LIFEPAC 10

MANAGEMENT

STRUCTURE OF THE LIFEPAC CURRICULUM

The LIFEPAC curriculum is conveniently structured to provide one teacher handbook containing teacher support material with answer keys and ten student worktexts for each subject at grade levels two through twelve. The worktext format of the LIFEPACs allows the student to read the textual information and complete workbook activities all in the same booklet. The easy to follow LIFEPAC numbering system lists the grade as the first number(s) and the last two digits as the number of the series. For example, the Language Arts LIFEPAC at the 6th grade level, 5th book in the series would be LA 605.

Each LIFEPAC is divided into 3 to 5 sections and begins with an introduction or overview of the booklet as well as a series of specific learning objectives to give a purpose to the study of the LIFEPAC. The introduction and objectives are followed by a vocabulary section which may be found at the beginning of each section at the lower levels, at the beginning of the LIFEPAC in the middle grades, or in the glossary at the high school level. Vocabulary words are used to develop word recognition and should not be confused with the spelling words introduced later in the LIFEPAC. The student should learn all vocabulary words before working the LIFEPAC sections to improve comprehension, retention, and reading skills.

Each activity or written assignment has a number for easy identification, such as 1.1. The first number corresponds to the LIFEPAC section and the number to the right of the decimal is the number of the activity.

Teacher checkpoints, which are essential to maintain quality learning, are found at various locations throughout the LIFEPAC. The teacher should check 1) neatness of work and penmanship, 2) quality of understanding (tested with a short oral quiz), 3) thoroughness of answers (complete sentences and paragraphs, correct spelling, etc.), 4) completion of activities (no blank spaces), and 5) accuracy of answers as compared to the answer key (all answers correct).

The self test questions are also number coded for easy reference. For example, 2.015 means that this is the 15th question in the self test of Section II. The first number corresponds to the LIFEPAC section, the zero indicates that it is a self test question, and the number to the right of the zero the question number.

The LIFEPAC test is packaged at the centerfold of each LIFEPAC. It should be removed and put aside before giving the booklet to the student for study.

Answer and test keys have the same numbering system as the LIFEPACs and appear at the back of this handbook. The student may be given access to the answer keys (not the test keys) under teacher supervision so that he can score his own work.

A thorough study of the Curriculum Overview by the teacher before instruction begins is essential to the success of the student. The teacher should become familiar with expected skill mastery and understand how these grade level skills fit into the overall skill development of the curriculum. The teacher should also preview the objectives that appear at the beginning of each LIFEPAC for additional preparation and planning.

TEST SCORING and GRADING

Answer keys and test keys give examples of correct answers. They convey the idea, but the student may use many ways to express a correct answer. The teacher should check for the essence of the answer, not for the exact wording. Many questions are high level and require thinking and creativity on the part of the student. Each answer should be scored based on whether or not the main idea written by the student matches the model example. "Any Order" or "Either Order" in a key indicates that no particular order is necessary to be correct.

Most self tests and LIFEPAC tests at the lower elementary levels are scored at 1 point per answers; however, the upper levels may have a point system awarding 2 to 5 points for various answers or questions. Further, the total test points will vary; they may not always equal 100 points. They may be 78, 85, 100, 105, etc.

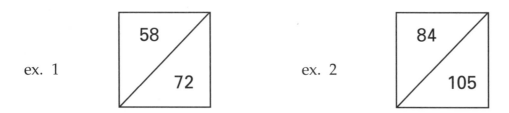

A score box similar to ex.1 above is located at the end of each self test and on the front of the LIFEPAC test. The bottom score, 72, represents the total number of points possible on the test. The upper score, 58, represents the number of points your student will need to receive an 80% or passing grade. If you wish to establish the exact percentage that your student has achieved, find the total points of his correct answers and divide it by the bottom number (in this case 72.) For example, if your student has a point total of 65, divide 65 by 72 for a grade of 90%. Referring to ex. 2, on a test with a total of 105 possible points, the student would have to receive a minimum of 84 correct points for an 80% or passing grade. If your student has received 93 points, simply divide the 93 by 105 for a percentage grade of 89%. Students who receive a score below 80% should review the LIFEPAC and retest using the appropriate Alternate Test found in the Teacher's Guide.

The following is a guideline to assign letter grades for completed LIFEPACs based on a maximum total score of 100 points.

LIFEPAC Test = 60% of the Total Score (or percent grade)
Self Test = 25% of the Total Score (average percent of self tests)
Reports = 10% or 10* points per LIFEPAC
Oral Work = 5% or 5* points per LIFEPAC
*Determined by the teacher's subjective evaluation of the student's daily work.

Example:

LIFEPAC Test Score	=	92%	92 x .60	=	55 points
Self Test Average	=	90%	90 x .25	=	23 points
Reports				=	8 points
Oral Work				=	4 points

TOTAL POINTS   =   90 points

Grade Scale based on point system:

100	–	94	=	A
93	–	86	=	B
85	–	77	=	C
76	–	70	=	D
Below		70	=	F

TEACHER HINTS and STUDYING TECHNIQUES

LIFEPAC Activities are written to check the level of understanding of the preceding text. The student may look back to the text as necessary to complete these activities; however, a student should never attempt to do the activities without reading (studying) the text first. Self tests and LIFEPAC tests are never open book tests.

Language arts activities (skill integration) often appear within other subject curriculum. The purpose is to give the student an opportunity to test his skill mastery outside of the context in which it was presented.

Writing complete answers (paragraphs) to some questions is an integral part of the LIFEPAC Curriculum in all subjects. This builds communication and organization skills, increases understanding and retention of ideas, and helps enforce good penmanship. Complete sentences should be encouraged for this type of activity. Obviously, single words or phrases do not meet the intent of the activity, since multiple lines are given for the response.

Review is essential to student success. Time invested in review where review is suggested will be time saved in correcting errors later. Self tests, unlike the section activities, are closed book. This procedure helps to identify weaknesses before they become too great to overcome. Certain objectives from self tests are cumulative and test previous sections; therefore, good preparation for a self test must include all material studied up to that testing point.

The following procedure checklist has been found to be successful in developing good study habits in the LIFEPAC curriculum.

1. Read the introduction and Table of Contents.
2. Read the objectives.
3. Recite and study the entire vocabulary (glossary) list.
4. Study each section as follows:
    a. Read the introduction and study the section objectives.
    b. Read all the text for the entire section, but answer none of the activities.
    c. Return to the beginning of the section and memorize each vocabulary word and definition.
    d. Reread the section, complete the activities, check the answers with the answer key, correct all errors, and have the teacher check.
    e. Read the self test but do not answer the questions.
    f. Go to the beginning of the first section and reread the text and answers to the activities up to the self test you have not yet done.
    g. Answer the questions to the self test without looking back.
    h. Have the self test checked by the teacher.
    i. Correct the self test and have the teacher check the corrections.
    j. Repeat steps a–i for each section.

5. Use the SQ3R* method to prepare for the LIFEPAC test.
6. Take the LIFEPAC test as a closed book test.
7. LIFEPAC tests are administered and scored under direct teacher supervision. Students who receive scores below 80% should review the LIFEPAC using the SQ3R* study method and take the Alternate Test located in the Teacher Handbook. The final test grade may be the grade on the Alternate Test or an average of the grades from the original LIFEPAC test and the Alternate Test.

   *SQ3R: Scan the whole LIFEPAC.
   Question yourself on the objectives.
   Read the whole LIFEPAC again.
   Recite through an oral examination.
   Review weak areas.

GOAL SETTING and SCHEDULES

Each school must develop its own schedule, because no single set of procedures will fit every situation. The following is an example of a daily schedule that includes the five LIFEPAC subjects as well as time slotted for special activities.

Possible Daily Schedule

8:15	–	8:25	Pledges, prayer, songs, devotions, etc.
8:25	–	9:10	Bible
9:10	–	9:55	Language Arts
9:55	–	10:15	Recess (juice break)
10:15	–	11:00	Mathematics
11:00	–	11:45	Social Studies
11:45	–	12:30	Lunch, recess, quiet time
12:30	–	1:15	Science
1:15	–		Drill, remedial work, enrichment*

*Enrichment: Computer time, physical education, field trips, fun reading, games and puzzles, family business, hobbies, resource persons, guests, crafts, creative work, electives, music appreciation, projects.

Basically, two factors need to be considered when assigning work to a student in the LIFEPAC curriculum.

The first is time. An average of 45 minutes should be devoted to each subject, each day. Remember, this is only an average. Because of extenuating circumstances a student may spend only 15 minutes on a subject one day and the next day spend 90 minutes on the same subject.

The second factor is the number of pages to be worked in each subject. A single LIFEPAC is designed to take 3 to 4 weeks to complete. Allowing about 3-4 days for LIFEPAC introduction, review, and tests, the student has approximately 15 days to complete the LIFEPAC pages. Simply take the number of pages in the LIFEPAC, divide it by 15 and you will have the number of pages that must be completed on a daily basis to keep the student on schedule. For example, a LIFEPAC containing 45 pages will require 3 completed pages per day. Again, this is only an average. While working a 45 page LIFEPAC, the student may complete only 1 page the first day if the text has a lot of activities or reports, but go on to complete 5 pages the next day.

Long range planning requires some organization. Because the traditional school year originates in the early fall of one year and continues to late spring of the following year, a calendar should be devised that covers this period of time. Approximate beginning and completion dates can be noted on the calendar as well as special occasions such as holidays, vacations and birthdays. Since each LIFEPAC takes 3-4 weeks or eighteen days to complete, it should take about 180 school days to finish a set of ten LIFEPACs. Starting at the beginning school date, mark off eighteen school days on the calendar and that will become the targeted completion date for the first LIFEPAC. Continue marking the calendar until you have established dates for the remaining nine LIFEPACs making adjustments for previously noted holidays and vacations. If all five subjects are being used, the ten established target dates should be the same for the LIFEPACs in each subject.

FORMS

The sample weekly lesson plan and student grading sheet forms are included in this section as teacher support materials and may be duplicated at the convenience of the teacher.

The student grading sheet is provided for those who desire to follow the suggested guidelines for assignment of letter grades found on page 3 of this section. The student's self test scores should be posted as percentage grades. When the LIFEPAC is completed the teacher should average the self test grades, multiply the average by .25 and post the points in the box marked self test points. The LIFEPAC percentage grade should be multiplied by .60 and posted. Next, the teacher should award and post points for written reports and oral work. A report may be any type of written work assigned to the student whether it is a LIFEPAC or additional learning activity. Oral work includes the student's ability to respond orally to questions which may or may not be related to LIFEPAC activities or any type of oral report assigned by the teacher. The points may then be totaled and a final grade entered along with the date that the LIFEPAC was completed.

The Student Record Book which was specifically designed for use with the Alpha Omega curriculum provides space to record weekly progress for one student over a nine week period as well as a place to post self test and LIFEPAC scores. The Student Record Books are available through the current Alpha Omega catalog; however, unlike the enclosed forms these books are not for duplication and should be purchased in sets of four to cover a full academic year.

WEEKLY LESSON PLANNER

Week of:

Subject	Subject	Subject	Subject
Monday			

Subject	Subject	Subject	Subject
Tuesday			

Subject	Subject	Subject	Subject
Wednesday			

Subject	Subject	Subject	Subject
Thursday			

Subject	Subject	Subject	Subject
Friday			

WEEKLY LESSON PLANNER

Week of:

	Subject	Subject	Subject	Subject
Monday				
	Subject	Subject	Subject	Subject
Tuesday				
	Subject	Subject	Subject	Subject
Wednesday				
	Subject	Subject	Subject	Subject
Thursday				
	Subject	Subject	Subject	Subject
Friday				

Student Name _____   Year _____

Bible

| LP # | Self Test Scores by Sections | | | | | Self Test Points | LIFEPAC Test | Oral Points | Report Points | Final Grade | Date |
	1	2	3	4	5						
01											
02											
03											
04											
05											
06											
07											
08											
09											
10											

History & Geography

| LP # | Self Test Scores by Sections | | | | | Self Test Points | LIFEPAC Test | Oral Points | Report Points | Final Grade | Date |
	1	2	3	4	5						
01											
02											
03											
04											
05											
06											
07											
08											
09											
10											

Language Arts

| LP # | Self Test Scores by Sections | | | | | Self Test Points | LIFEPAC Test | Oral Points | Report Points | Final Grade | Date |
	1	2	3	4	5						
01											
02											
03											
04											
05											
06											
07											
08											
09											
10											

Student Name _____   Year _____

Mathematics

LP #	Self Test Scores by Sections 1	2	3	4	5	Self Test Points	LIFEPAC Test	Oral Points	Report Points	Final Grade	Date
01											
02											
03											
04											
05											
06											
07											
08											
09											
10											

Science

LP #	Self Test Scores by Sections 1	2	3	4	5	Self Test Points	LIFEPAC Test	Oral Points	Report Points	Final Grade	Date
01											
02											
03											
04											
05											
06											
07											
08											
09											
10											

Spelling/Electives

LP #	Self Test Scores by Sections 1	2	3	4	5	Self Test Points	LIFEPAC Test	Oral Points	Report Points	Final Grade	Date
01											
02											
03											
04											
05											
06											
07											
08											
09											
10											

TEACHER

N
O
T
E
S

INSTRUCTIONS FOR SCIENCE

The LIFEPAC curriculum from grades two through twelve is structured so that the daily instructional material is written directly into the LIFEPACs. The student is encouraged to read and follow this instructional material in order to develop independent study habits. The teacher should introduce the LIFEPAC to the student, set a required completion schedule, complete teacher checks, be available for questions regarding both content and procedures, administer and grade tests, and develop additional learning activities as desired. Teachers working with several students may schedule their time so that students are assigned to a quiet work activity when it is necessary to spend instructional time with one particular student.

The Teacher Notes section of the Teacher's Guide lists the required or suggested materials for the LIFEPACs and provides additional learning activities for the students. The materials section refers only to LIFEPAC materials and does not include materials which may be needed for the additional activities. Additional learning activities provide a change from the daily school routine, encourage the student's interest in learning and may be used as a reward for good study habits.

If you have limited facilities and are not able to perform all the experiments contained in the LIFEPAC curriculum, the Science Project List for grades 3-12 may be a useful tool for you. This list prioritizes experiments into three categories: those essential to perform, those which should be performed as time and facilities permit, and those not essential for mastery of LIFEPACs. Of course, for complete understanding of concepts and student participation in the curriculum, all experiments should be performed whenever practical. Materials for the experiments are shown in Teacher Notes – Materials Needed.

Science Projects List

Key

(1) = Those essential to perform for basic understanding of scientific principles.

(2) = Those which should be performed as time permits.

(3) = Those not essential for mastery of LIFEPACs.

S = Equipment needed for home school or Christian school lab.

E = Explanation or demonstration by instructor may replace student or class lab work.

H = Suitable for homework or for home school students. (No lab equipment needed.)

Science 701

pp			
	5	(1)	H
	9	(2)	S

Science 702

pp			
	14	(1)	S
	17-19	(1)	S

Science 703

pp			
	7	(1)	H
	14	(2)	S or H
	15	(1)	S
	19	(2)	E
	34	(1)	S
	35	(2)	S
	39	(2)	S
	45	(1)	S

Science 704

pp			
	24	(1)	S
	32	(2)	H
	33-35	(1)	S
	44	(1)	S

Science 705

pp			
	11	(1)	S

Science 706

pp			
	6	(1)	H
	17	(1)	S

Science 707

None

Science 708

pp			
	4	(1)	S
	28	(1)	H
	31	(2)	H
	33	(1)	H

Science 709

pp			
	7	(1)	S
	13	(1)	H
	15	(1)	H
	26	(2)	H

Science 710

pp			
	5	(1)	H

Materials Need for LIFEPAC

Required:
None

Suggested:
box containing a variety of objects for
  students to classify--For example:
  a nail, a piece of wood, a tin can, a seed,
  a piece of cloth, a sponge,
  a comb, a stone, a pencil, a plastic bag,
  a book of matches, and so on
a book or other resource with information
  about George Washington Carver

Additional Learning Activities

Section I Tools of a Scientist

1. Arrange ten objects on a tray. Show the tray to a group of friends for fifteen seconds and cover the tray. Ask your friends to list as many of the objects as they can remember.
2. Gather leaves from ten different plants. List as many similarities and differences as possible. Name ways to classify your leaves.

Section II Methods of a Scientist

1. Show the student(s) a magazine picture and ask the students to write as many questions as they can about the picture.
2. With a friend use the scientific method to solve a problem.
3. Write a skit involving a problem. Solve the problem with the scientific method. Present the skit to the rest of the class.
4. Make a poster illustrating the scientific method.
5. Write a one-page report on the importance of curiosity to a scientist.

Section III Work of a Scientist

1. Discuss the ways scientists have improved the quality of life. Topics might include: curing disease, predicting earthquakes and volcanic eruptions, developing varieties of plants that produce higher yields, forecasting the weather, and so on.
2. Make a bulletin board of famous scientists and their contributions.
3. Select one famous Christian scientist and write a one-page report about him. You may use an encyclopedia or other library books for this assignment.

Section IV Careers in Science

1. Discuss with the students the difference between a technician and an engineer (Training differences can be seen in a university catalog or a junior college catalog.)
2. Read a brief biography of a scientist in an encyclopedia. With friends act out an important event in the life of that scientist.
3. Look in pamphlets like those from the federal or state governments, colleges, or Metropolitan Life Insurance Co. Select one field of science and read about different occupations within that field.
4. Make a poster using the information given in Section IV to illustrate the need for scientists.

Materials Needed for LIFEPAC

Required:
centimeter ruler
meter stick
straight pins
graduated cylinder
small rock
six to eight containers of various sizes--
    orange juice cans, 303 size cans, soup
    cans, tuna fish cans, Spam cans, or
    different glass or plastic containers
nail
rubber band
ruler; does not have to be metric
medicine cups
modeling clay
jar lids or wooden blocks
watering can with a spout

Suggested:
None

Additional Learning Activities

Section I Measurement

1. Demonstrate the simplicity of the metric system as compared to the English system by measuring items in a cookbook recipe and multiplying the recipe for a larger group.

2. The student may wish to use a stopwatch to see how far he can walk or run in a given time. The distance he covers would be measured to the nearest meter. He may also use a stopwatch for a number of similar tasks, such as finding how the speed of a marble running down an inclined plane is affected by the incline of the plane. The speeds would be expressed as meters or centimeters per second. Graph the results.

3. With the class plan a Mini Olympics. Divide the class into four well-matched teams. The amount of time you spend on each competition and the number of events you schedule will determine whether each team participates in each event. Select measurers, recorders, and referees for each event. You may rotate your teams to do this task. While Team A participates in the discus throw, Team B will act as measurers, recorders, and referees.

Materials needed for Mini Olympics.

Suggested Activity	Material or Equipment
discus throw	paper plates or cardboard discs
shot put	wad of newspaper
javelin throw	plastic drinking straw
basket shot	wastebasket, Nerf ball
torch relay	crepe-paper-decorated baton
chariot race	four boys carrying a fifth on a tumbling mat

4. The student may write and solve practical problems involving areas. Typical problems might include the following ones: If a can of paint covers 100 square meters, how many cans of paint are needed to paint a wall that is 15 meters high and 40 meters long? Students could figure how many cans of paint would be needed to cover their classroom walls.

5. Student(s) may be asked to estimate some lengths, (the height of a desk, for example) then measure it to see how good the estimate was.

Section II Graphing Data

1. Show the student(s) several examples of graphs that have been clipped from magazines or newspapers.

2. Assign a group of students a set of data and have them make four different kinds of graphs using the same data.

3. Conduct a survey in your class asking one question and graph the data you gather. For example, the question may be, "Do you live in the country or in town?" or "How many children are there in your family?"

4. Find a graph in the encyclopedia, a magazine, or a newspaper. Use the data from that graph and make another kind of graph.

Materials Needed for LIFEPAC

Required:
cardboard or heavy construction paper
scissors
paper fasteners
encyclopedia or other reference books
salt cartons, the twenty-six ounce size
flashlight
nails of different sizes
books or blocks of wood to support lenses
waxed paper or tissue paper
convex lenses of different focal lengths
     (different size magnifying lenses)
candle
chewing gum or modeling clay
drinking straw
rubber bands
thread
blocks of wood (13 x 8 x 1 1/2 cm),
     (20 x 20 x 3 cm), (20 x 3 x 3 cm)
metal washers
pieces of tin; orange juice cans or other tin
   that can easily be cut
protractors, half-circle and full-circle
nails (5 cm and 4 cm)
glue

Suggested:
styrofoam ball
umbrella
magnet
small plastic bags large enough to
   hold magnet
glass jar or other glass container
medicine dropper
microscope
concave mirror like a magnifying
make-up mirror
corrugated cardboard, any heavy cardboard
thumbtacks
fishline or string

Additional Learning Activities

Section I Stargazing

1. With poster board and paints or colored paper construct a chart comparing the geocentric theory to the heliocentric theory of the universe.
2. The closer a star is to an observer the brighter it appears to be. Illustrate this point with two flashlights, one dim and one bright. Position one child with the bright flashlight some distance away. Have another child stand nearby with the dim flashlight. The closer child's light will appear brighter even though he has the dimmer light.
3. Make a booklet using fluorescent stars (available in variety stores) and dark construction paper to diagram different constellations.
4. Find Mars, Jupiter, Venus, or Saturn in the night sky (an almanac will tell you when these planets are visible). Observe the "wanderings" of these planets for several nights. Write a summary of your observations.

Section II Astronomy

1. Make a bulletin board about great scientists and their contributions to astronomy.
2. Have a contest with a classmate to name as many elliptical objects as you can.
3. Make a time line of famous astronomical discoveries.
4. With the astrolabe made in class, record the altitude of several prominent stars or the moon on several different clear nights.
5. Write a one-page report about one of these scientists: Aristotle, Ptolemy, Aristarchus, Copernicus, Brahe, Kepler, Newton, Jansky.

Materials Needed for LIFEPAC

Required:
package-sealing tape or reinforced
   strapping tape
scissors
construction paper or banner paper

Suggested:
bicycle wheel
chalk
circle of corrugated cardboard,
   30 cm in diameter
banner paper or several sheets of
   construction paper taped together
string
protractor
red and black pencils
banner paper or any large sheet
   of white paper
compass

ADDITIONAL LEARNING ACTIVITIES

Section I The Sun's Energy

1. Discuss the possible results if the sun were to explode and lose some of its mass.
2. Demonstrate the relationship between the distance from the sun and the amount of solar radiation received. You will need a 100-watt light bulb, a socket, a light meter (borrowed from a photographer), a meter stick, and graph paper. See figure below.

3. Construct a display of energy-saving devices. This might include items that require human energy rather than manufactured energy.
4. Using an encyclopedia or some other reference book study about one of these scientists and write a one-page report about his life and work: Hermann von Helmholtz, Albert Einstein, Hans A. Bethe.
5. Make a poster depicting the benefits of the sun's energy.
6. Make a graph representing your idea of how the amount of energy released by the sun changes with the passing of time.

Section II The Sun's Family

1. Create a mural depicting the planets, asteroids, and comets in the solar system.
2. Consult an almanac to learn when the next meteor shower will occur. Watch with a group of friends so a large area of the sky may be observed. Record the number of meteors you see.
3. Use a telescope to observe the planets.
4. Consult an almanac to learn when the planets will be visible and observe their change of position during several nights.
5. Use an encyclopedia to learn the sizes of the other moons in our solar system. Prepare a chart that compares our moon's size to the others.
6. Write a report about the rings of Saturn. What is their composition? Do other planets have a similar set of rings?

Section III The Moon

1. Construct a model with wire and styrofoam balls to show the inclination of the moon's orbit to the plane of the earth's orbit.
2. Make a diagram showing where low and high tides occur in relation to the moon's position.
3. Collect photographs of the moon and display them on a poster or in a scrapbook.
4. Observe and record the time of moonrise and moonset during the various phases of the moon.

Section IV Eclipses

1. Demonstrate an eclipse with a globe, a ball, and an electric light.
2. Learn that a circular object casts a round shadow with a ball, a square object, and a projector or flashlight. How would this investigation relate to the theory that the earth is round?
3. Make a chart to show the difference between a partial and a total eclipse.
4. Use an encyclopedia or almanac to learn how often eclipses occur and prepare a table showing this information.

Materials Needed for LIFEPAC

Required:
shoe boxes
thermometers
sheet of clear plastic or glass
cellophane wrap
stopwatch; any watch that has a
    second hand
pan; 20 to 30 cm diameter by 5 cm deep
metric ruler

Suggested:
None

ADDITIONAL LEARNING ACTIVITIES

Section I Structure of the Atmosphere

1. Select one of the gases from Figure 2 Section I of the LIFEPAC to write a one-page report about. Use an encyclopedia or another reference book to find information for the report.
2. Using an encyclopedia compare the summer and winter temperatures of several states and countries to determine whether they gain or lose more radiation. Prepare a chart or table to show the results of your study.

Section II Natural Cycles

1. Demonstrate the carbon-oxygen cycle by sealing a snail and an aquarium plant such as *Anacharis* (elodea) in a test tube or baby food jar. (Both organisms may be obtained at any pet or variety store that has tropical fish.)
2. Illustrate the principles involved in the water cycle with a distillation apparatus. You will need a flask that has been fitted with a one-hole stopper, a U-shaped piece of glass tubing, and a test tube resting in a beaker of ice water.

3. Obtain the roots of alfalfa, clover, peanut, or other legume plants. Study the swellings or nodules on these roots. They contain thousands of nitrogen-fixing bacteria.

4. Students may study the effects of nitrogen-fixing bacteria on plant growth in the classroom. Sterilize four small flowerpots of soil in an oven (320° to 375° for at least one hour). When the soil has cooled, add nitrogen-fixing bacteria (purchased from a seed company) to the soil in two of the flowerpots. Soak clover seeds in water for several hours and add equal quantities of the seeds to each of the four pots. Observe the growth for several weeks. In which pots do the students notice the healthiest clover plants? Transpiration may be observed in a growing plant by covering the soil in the pot with plastic wrap and placing the plant under a large glass jar in bright sunlight. Within fifteen minutes a film of water will form on the inside of the jar. (The plastic wrap is necessary to prevent the evaporation of soil water.)

5. Write a report on seeding clouds with dry ice or iodized salts to produce rain.

Section III Pollution

1. The effects of sulfur oxides on a living plant may be demonstrated by melting a small amount of powdered sulfur (available at drug stores) in a closed container with a plant. Geraniums are especially good for this demonstration. For a control, place a second geranium in a closed container but do not melt the sulfur in the control. After a few days the effects of the sulfur gas will be dramatic as the plant turns brown and dies. Note: This experiment should only be conducted by the teacher. Inhaling large amounts of the gas is dangerous.

2. Prepare a bulletin board on some aspect of the air pollution problem. For instance, you might consider the causes of pollution, the results of pollution, or ways to control pollution as possible themes.

3. Study about the composition of glass, metal cans, and newspaper. Write a one-page report on what is saved when these items are recycled.

4. Clip articles about pollution from newspapers and magazines and make a pollution scrapbook.

Materials Needed for LIFEPAC

Required:
atlas
shiny metal can; any unlabeled tin can
thermometer
wind vane
barometer
hygrometer
anemometer
rain gauge

Suggested:
None

Additional Learning Activities

Section I Elements of Weather

1. Demonstrate the use of these weather instruments as available: anemometer, high-low thermometer, barometer, wind vane, hygrometer.

2. Study the temperature variations at different distances about the earth. You will need three thermometers, a wooden stake (four and one-half feet long), and masking tape. Pound the stake into the ground. Attach the thermometers with masking tape at heights of 4 inches, 18 inches, and 48 inches. Read all three thermometers hourly and record the readings. Conduct the experiment on three different days: a calm, sunny day; a sunny, windy day; and a cloudy day. Compare the variation of temperature with height on each day.

3. Make a simple thermometer. You will need a flask, a one-hole rubber stopper that fits the flask, a piece of glass tubing, and a bottle of food coloring. Insert the glass tubing through the hole in the rubber stopper. Fill the flask with water and add a drop of food coloring. Placing the stopper in the neck of the flask will force the colored water into the glass tubing. Mark the water level on the glass tubing. As the temperature changes the water level will change also.

4. Make a simple barometer. You will need two small jars (baby food jars), rubber bands, a balloon, transparent tape, a drinking straw, a six-inch wooden stick, and a level platform where the barometer can remain undisturbed for several days. Set the barometer up as shown below. Mark the movements of the straw pointer on the wooden stick. Observe and record data for several days.

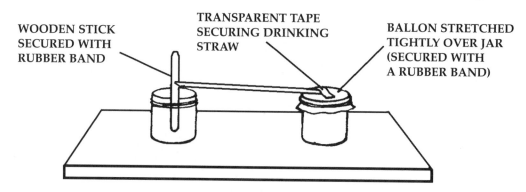

WOODEN STICK
SECURED WITH
RUBBER BAND

TRANSPARENT TAPE
SECURING DRINKING
STRAW

BALLON STRETCHED
TIGHTLY OVER JAR
(SECURED WITH
A RUBBER BAND)

5. Write a paragraph about each of the main elements of weather (temperature, wind, pressure, and moisture). Include how each element is formed and describe the instruments that can be used to measure each.

6. Use an encyclopedia to learn about the Beaufort scale and write a one-page report about it.

Section II Weather in Motion

1. Demonstrate cloud formation. You will need a jar containing 50 ml of hot water, a match, and a plastic bag containing two or three ice cubes. Light the match and hold it over the jar of hot water. Drop the match in the jar and quickly cover the top of the jar with the bag of ice cubes. Study the jar closely to observe a "cloud" form as water vapor condenses on the smoke particles.

2. Make a table of the different fronts according to shape, type of clouds, type of precipitation, and the air masses involved.

3. Draw a diagram to show cloud formations and the altitudes at which they are located.

4. Consult an encyclopedia and write a report on the hurricanes of North America.

5. Collect pictures of cloud formations and mount them in a scrapbook with a description of each.

Section III Weather Forecasting

1. Visit a local weather bureau or weather station.

2. Discuss some weather sayings with the student(s) and determine which are useful and which are based on superstition.

3. Study the station model in Section III of the LIFEPAC. Make up a station model of your own and give it to a friend to interpret.

4. Research cloud seeding and the laws that govern it. Write a report on your findings.

5. Make a weather map and label the symbols you use.

6. Clip a weather map from a newspaper. Mount the map on a poster and write a description to explain the numbers and symbols.

Science 707 Teacher Notes

Materials Needed for LIFEPAC
Required:
Atlas

Suggested:
None

Additional Learning Activities
Section I Climate
1. Use information from an encyclopedia or almanac to show how average temperatures vary within the United States.
2. Construct a bulletin board depicting the four elements of a climate.
3. Make a map of the United States showing the average temperatures for a city in each state.
4. Write a report on the causes of the wind, air pressure, precipitation, and temperature.
5. Write a report on this topic: "Which affects me more, the weather or the climate?" (Which do you notice more changes in?)

Section II Climate: World Wide
1. Make a large map of the world and label the general climactic areas.
2. Make a map with isotherms or isobars. Give the map to a friend and ask him to interpret it.
3. Use an encyclopedia to find the altitudes of the following cities or geographical locations: Death Valley, California; Innsbruck, Austria; Santiago, Chile; Beijing, China; Cape Town, South Africa; and Denver, Colorado. Make a chart to show the altitudes and mean annual temperatures of each place.

Section III Climate: Regional
1. Consult a daily newspaper and keep a weather chart on five cities for one week. Select one city in a desert climate, one in a steppes climate, one in a mountain climate, one in a mediterranean climate, and one in a humid subtropical climate.
2. Cut pictures from magazines to illustrate the types of animals and vegetation you would find in a specific climate. Mount the pictures on poster board and label each item.
3. Refer to an encyclopedia or other library book to learn what life is like on a banana plantation. Write a one-page report on the information you find.
4. Use an encyclopedia to study different types of housing and draw examples of each. Display your drawings in the classroom.

Section IV Climate: Local
1. Read about the aborigines of Australia and write a report on them and their climate.
2. Choose some places you would like to visit and find out what type of climates they have. Write a short paragraph about each place.

Materials Needed for LIFEPAC

Required:
wooden splints or toothpicks
coverslips
glass slides
medicine dropper
iodine solution (If Lugol's iodine
   solution is not available,
   methylene blue from a pet
   store can be substituted.)
microscope
tweezers
bright lamp or flashlight
hand mirror

Suggested:
apple
potato
blindfold

Additional Learning Activities

Section I Human Building Blocks

1. Gain more experience in microscopy by obtaining pond or river water to study. Many one-celled organisms can be found in this water.
2. Consult an encyclopedia to learn about inherited traits. Use one trait such as hair color and make a survey of your classmates to study the frequency of dark hair and light hair.
3. From a picture in an encyclopedia or other book make a diagram of the DNA molecule to display in your classroom.
4. Use an encyclopedia to learn about the work of Robert Hooke or Anton van Leeuwenhoek. Write a one-page report about their study of cells.
5. Make a poster depicting the levels of organization in living organisms. Include an example of a tissue, an organ, and a system found in the human body.

Section II Human Framework

1. Obtain a meatless leg bone from a meat market. Ask the butcher to cut it longitudinally. Identify the parts of the bone.
2. Obtain some muscle tissue from a meat market. Study a tiny portion of the tissue under the microscope. Include both voluntary and involuntary muscles in your observations.
3. Study a first aid book and prepare an oral report on the treatment of broken bones, sprains, strains, and dislocations.
4. Consult an encyclopedia to learn about the Achilles tendon and write a short report about Achilles.
5. Write a report on the use of fingerprints as a means of identification.

Section III Human Nervous System

1. Diagram the human brain on a blackboard or bulletin board and write the activities controlled by each part.
2. Place twenty common objects in a box. Blindfold a group of students and have them identify the items with their sense of touch.

3. Prepare four solutions; sugar and water, salt and water, vinegar and water, and a very weak solution of aspirin in water. Use a camel's hair brush to put drops of the solutions on the tongue. Identify the areas of the tongue that are responsive to sweet, salty, sour, and bitter tastes.

4. Make a list of 25 different response-stimulus reactions you experience in one day.

5. Make a poster showing the structure of the eye or ear. Label the parts and display the finished poster in the classroom.

6. Consult an encyclopedia and write a three-page report on the structure and function of the nervous system.

Materials Needed for LIFEPAC

Required:
glass slides
medicine dropper
sink or large pan
watch with a second hand

Suggested:
white bread or crackers

Additional Learning Activities

Section I The Respiratory System

1. Demonstrate the capacity of the lungs with a gallon jug, a two-hole rubber stopper, two pieces of glass tubing, ink or food coloring, and a graduated cylinder. Arrange the apparatus as shown in Figure 4. Each student should inhale as deeply as he can and exhale into the glass tube.

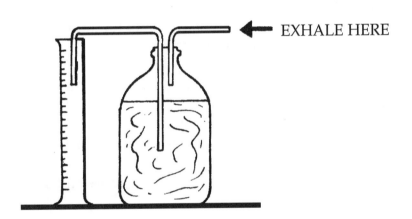

EXHALE HERE

2. Discuss which substance man can live the longest without: food, water, or oxygen.
3. Construct a chart to show the flow of blood through the heart and lungs.
4. Use an encyclopedia to learn more about the larynx and prepare a presentation to give in front of the class.
5. Write a report on the respiration problems astronauts must deal with in space.
6. Ask a friend to count your respiration rate. Run in place for two minutes and count the number of breaths you take in the next minute. Inhale and exhale into a paper bag and count your respiration rate again (the medulla which regulates breathing is stimulated by the increased carbon dioxide in the paper bag). Record the respiration rate for each test.

Section II The Circulatory System

1. Make a poster to illustrate the flow of blood through the heart.
2. Gather data on the relationship between age and heart rate. Check the pulse rates of younger children, parents, and grandparents and record the student(s) data on a large chart.

3. Consult an encyclopedia or other books to learn about the work of William Harvey. Write a one-page report on the circulation of the blood.

4. The human heart is about the size of your fist. To understand the pumping action of the heart make a tight fist and open your hand at a rate of seventy-two times a minute.

Section III The Digestive System

1. Stimulate a classroom discussion by asking two students to stretch out a twenty-foot length of rope. The length of rope is approximately as long as the intestine. Ask the students these questions. How does food move through the digestive system? How does the food change as it moves through the body? How does the food get from the digestive tract into the bloodstream?

2. Make a chart on the blackboard listing the organs involved in the digestive process and ask the students to explain the role of each organ in digestion.

3. Commercial meat tenderizers contain an enzyme, papain, which is extracted from papayas. Discuss how tenderizing meat with this enzyme would aid digestion.

4. Make a diagram to show the path of food through the digestive system.

5. Learn if your community has fluoridated water.

6. In your own words explain why food goes down your esophagus and not the trachea. Show your explanation to the teacher.

Section IV The Excretory System

1. Demonstrate the cooling effect of evaporation by wiping the skin on a student's arm with a cotton ball that has been soaked in isopropyl (rubbing) alcohol. Notice that the alcohol evaporates and removes heat from the surface of the skin.

2. Write a report to describe the structures and general location of the urinary system.

3. Consult an encyclopedia or other books for information on kidney transplants and prepare an oral presentation to give in front of the class.

Section V The Endocrine System

1. Hormones to control growth are also produced in plants. Buy some gibberellic acid at a greenhouse or nursery and apply it to pea seeds or to the shoots of young pea plant seedlings. Record your observations and discuss the final results after several weeks.

2. Construct a bulletin board to show the locations and functions of the glands of the endocrine system.

3. Use the library to learn about one of these hormones and write a one-page report about it: thyroid hormone, parathorhome, ACTH, oxytocin, cortin, and epinephrine.

4. Consult an encyclopedia for information on giantism and dwarfism. Write a report on your findings.

Materials Needed for LIFEPAC

Required:
celery
water glass or quart jar
teaspoon
red food coloring
knife

Suggested:
None

Additional Learning Activities

Section I Scientists at Work

1. Present the students with a problem to solve using the scientific method. Possible problems might be: Do plants have to have soil to grow? How can the height of a tree be determined without actually measuring it?
2. Measure 15 objects in your classroom and record your metric measurements.
3. Prepare newspaper articles about famous scientists as if they were making their discoveries today. Perhaps you can have your newspaper copied for other classes to read.
4. Measure the height of every student in your class in metric units. Make a bar graph with the number of students on the horizontal axis and the heights (disregard fractions of a unit) on the vertical axis.
5. Make a set of flash cards on the metric prefixes and basic units. Use the cards to quiz another student or as review for yourself.
6. Use a map to learn the distance from your home to ten different places and convert the mileage into metric units.

Section II The Astronomer At Work

1. Discuss the facts and fallacies of the five theories of solar energy.
2. Study the formation of craters by dropping objects of various sizes and shapes into dry plaster of Paris.
3. Construct a bulletin board to explain the phases of the moon.
4. Consult an encyclopedia or other library book to learn about one of the spacecraft missions. Write a report about one of these space exploration projects. Consult the latest edition of the World Almanac.
5. Select one of the following stars as a topic for a one-page written paper: the sun, Polaris, Sirius, Betelgeuse, Vega, Pollux, or Castor.

Section III The Meteorologist At Work

1. Prepare a large map to show where the different air masses form.
2. Designate a group of students as "weather team of the week." They will be responsible for giving a short weather report at the beginning of each class period.
3. Make a poster depicting the four classes of weather fronts and the type of weather that is associated with each class.
4. Consult an encyclopedia or other library book and write a report on the operation of weather satellites.

Section IV The Medical Scientist At Work

1. Make a matching chart on one of the following systems and use the chart to quiz other members of the class. (A matching chart consists of a picture or drawing of a system and a set of labeled cards that another student matches to various points on the picture.) Choose as a topic: how the heart and lungs work together; arteries, veins, and capillaries; the skeletal system; the nervous system, the digestive system; or the endocrine system.
2. Examine blood cells under a microscope.
3. Make a collection of items that have motions that resemble skeletal joints. For example, a hinge is similar to the elbow and a ball and socket is similar to the hip joint. Show the items you collect to the rest of the class.
4. Use the library to learn about a disease that affects one of the systems of the body and write a two-page report.

ADDITIONAL ACTIVITY KEY

ADDITIONAL ACTIVITY
This Activity may be reproduced as a student worksheet.

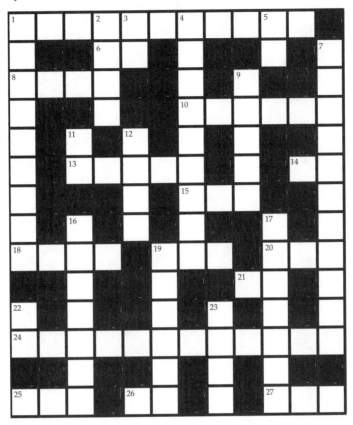

Across

1. Breathing in and out
6. United States (abbr.)
8. Basic unit of life
10. Brightest star
13. Dwarf planet discovered in 1930
14. A conjunction
15. A large unit of weight (English unit)
18. Form of precipitation
19. Opposite of many
20. What you must do to get energy
21. Milliliter (abbr.)
24. Something controlled by cerebellum
25. Number of natural satellites earth has
26. Opposite of out
27. Energy source for all life on earth

Down

1. Nerve endings in the skin
2. Contains blood vessels and nerves of the tooth
3. To be
4. Greek who believed in the geocentric theory
5. Opposite of off
7. A close inspection
9. Most complicated part of the body
11. Air mass that begins over north ocean (abbr.)
12. Same as 2 down
16. Chemical produced by endocrine glands
17. He invented temperature scale
19. The joining of two atoms
22. Cubic centimeter (abbr.)
23. A comet always has a head and a _____.

T
E
S
T
S

Reproducible Tests
for use with the Science 700
Teacher's Guide

Name _____

Answer *true* or *false* (each answer, 1 point).
1. _____ Observation involves a careful examination of things around us.
2. _____ The inductive method is a process of beginning with many particulars and proceeding to a generalization.
3. _____ Living things depend on other living things.
4. _____ Chemists tell us how things work, e.g. how a camera works.
5. _____ Philosophers are concerned about how man's mind works.
6. _____ Classification tells us the length and weight of something.
7. _____ Psychologists study human and animal behavior.
8. _____ Anthropologists study man's culture.
9. _____ Geology is a biological science.
10. _____ An experiment is a trial or test to discover something unknown.

Complete these statements (each answer, 3 points).
11. When making observations, man has _____ that he uses.
12. An inference is a _____ .
13. When a scientist makes a reasonable guess about the answer to a problem, he makes a _____ .
14. The sciences that are concerned with the nature of the universe are called _____ .
15. The biological sciences are concerned with the study of_____
_____ .
16. The process of orderly observation and thinking is _____ .
17. The study of the relationships of living things to each other and their environment is called _____ .
18. The branch of biology concerned with plant life is _____ .
19. The work of _____ was to change agriculture in the south.

Match these items (each answer, 2 points).
20._____ classification
21._____ data
22._____ measurement
23._____ questions
24._____ Antoine Lavoisier
25._____ Isaac Newton
26._____ Albert Einstein
27._____ Anton van Leewenhoek
28._____ Galileo
29._____ Carolus Linnaeus

a. found no gain or loss in chemical reactions
b. information
c. studied water with microscope
d. Law of Gravitation
e. determining length, weight, and volume
f. system of classification
g. systematic arrangement
h. wondering about phenomena
i. solar system and telescope
j. Law of Relativity

Write *1* before each physical science, write *2* before each biological science, and write *3* before each social science (each answer, 2 points).

30.
a. _____ anthropology   g. _____ geology

b. _____ astronomy   h. _____ meteorology

c. _____ botany   i. _____ paleontology

d. _____ chemistry   j. _____ physics

e. _____ ecology   k. _____ sociology

f. _____ geography   l. _____ zoology

Circle the correct answer (each answer, 2 points).

31.   All human hands have a thumb. Bill is a human child. Therefore, Bill has a thumb. This example illustrates (inductive, deductive) reasoning.

32.   Ann lives in Greenville. Everyone who lives in Greenville has a garden. Therefore, Ann has a garden. This example illustrates (inductive, deductive) reasoning.

Write the definitions (each answer, 5 points).

33.   a. Classification_____

_____

_____

b. Theory_____

_____

_____

_____

Complete these activities (each answer, 2 points).

34.   List three ways in which a horse and a dog are alike.

a. _____

b. _____

c. _____

35.   List three ways in which a horse and a dog are different.

a. _____

b. _____

c. _____

$\frac{86}{107}$

Date _____

Score _____

Name _____

Match these items (each answer, 2 points).

1. _____ mass
2. _____ weight
3. _____ gravity
4. _____ gram
5. _____ measurement
6. _____ length
7. _____ volume
8. _____ diameter
9. _____ circumference
10. _____ area
11. _____ metric system

    a. unit of mass
    b. distance around a circle
    c. distance across a circle
    d. surface covered
    e. decimal measurement system
    f. distance from point to point
    g. quantity of matter
    h. finding how far or how much
    i. space occupied
    j. attraction of gravity
    k. measured by weight

Match these items (each answer, 2 points).

12. _____ m, mm, km, cm
13. _____ L, ml
14. _____ kg, g
15. _____ cm^2, m^2, km^2
16. _____ m^3, cm^3

    a. units of length measurement
    b. units of volume measurement
    c. units of mass measurement
    d. units of area measurement

Complete the following sentences (each answer, 3 points).

17. The _____ is a decimal system of measurement.
18. Area and volume are determined from measurements of _____ .
19. _____ is the force that pulls all objects toward the center of the earth.
20. The force of gravity is measured by _____ .
21. When we make measurements we are making comparisons with a _____ .
22. _____ lose precision when they are plotted.
23. No matter where an object is its _____ remains constant.
24. Pictographs are similar to _____ .
25. An axis that is perpendicular to the horizontal axis is the _____ .

Answer *true* or *false* (each answer, 1 point).

26. _____ The United States uses decimal currency.
27. _____ The area of a rectangle is found by adding the length of the sides.
28. _____ A cubic centimeter of water is the same volume as a milliliter of water.
29. _____ A circle graph is a good way to compare parts with a whole.

Complete this activity (each item, 4 points).

30.   List the four types of graphs and show an example of each on a
        separate sheet of paper.

        a. _____

        b. _____

        c. _____

        d. _____

Complete the information requested (each answer, 1 point).

31.   Measure the length of each line segment to the nearest cm.

        a. AD _____   d. AB _____

        b. BC _____   e. AC _____

        c. DB _____

Answer the questions by reading the graph (each answer, 3 points).

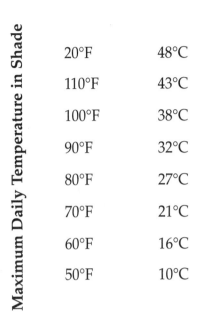

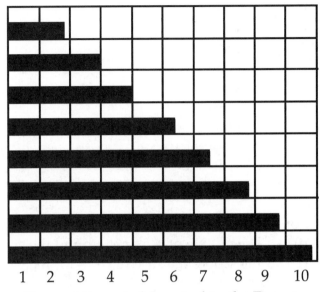

Maximum Daily Temperature in Shade

20°F	48°C
110°F	43°C
100°F	38°C
90°F	32°C
80°F	27°C
70°F	21°C
60°F	16°C
50°F	10°C

1 2 3 4 5 6 7 8 9 10

Days of Expected Survival in the Desert
(no walking, one quart of water available)

32. The graph above is a _____ graph.
33. When the temperature reaches 43°C, how long can the person expect to survive while sitting still? _____
34. What is the Celsius temperature, when a person can expect to survive 5.5 days? _____
35. At 70°F or 21°C a person could survive _____ days under the conditions of this graph.

Date _____
Score _____

55

Name _____

Match these items (each answer, 2 points).

1. _____ Galileo
2. _____ Cygnus
3. _____ meteoroid
4. _____ zenith
5. _____ Orion
6. _____ Ursa Major
7. _____ ellipse
8. _____ Copernicus
9. _____ Aristotle

a. heliocentric theory
b. Big Dipper
c. mass of rock in space
d. the Harp
e. Northern Cross
f. opposite of nadir
g. Betelguese
h. geocentric theory
i. orbit of planet
j. "Father of Modern Science"

Complete these statements (each answer, 3 points).

10. The motion of a planet around the sun is called a/an_____.

11. Telescopes that use mirrors for focusing light are called_____ telescopes.

12. The oval orbits traced by planets as they travel around the sun are_____.

13. An astronomical instrument used for measuring the altitude of the sun and stars is a/an_____.

14. The height of a star, planet, or other heavenly body in the sky is its_____.

15. A mass of rock or metal that enters the earth's atmosphere is a/an_____.

16. Elements in the stars can be identified by means of the_____.

Answer these questions (each numbered item, 5 points).

17. What are Kepler's three Laws of Planetary Motion?

   a. _____

   b. _____

   c. _____

18. Why are the motions that we observe in the heavens only apparent motions?

   _____

   _____

   _____

Complete these activities (each numbered item, 5 points).

19. Draw and label diagrams of the geocentric theory and the heliocentric theory.

20. Write an illustration of how the laws of gravitation and motion explain the motions of heavenly bodies. _____

_____

21. List three flaws in the transparent sphere hypothesis.

    a. _____

    b. _____

    c. _____

22. List two reasons why the "wanderers" created problems in the geocentric theory.

    a. _____

    b. _____

Date _____

Score _____

Name _____

Answer *true* or *false* (each answer, 1 point).
1. _____ The tail of a comet always points toward the sun.
2. _____ The energy that turns the blades of a windmill is derived from solar energy.
3. _____ The 29 1/2-day interval from new moon to new moon is called a lunar month.
4. _____ Asteroids orbit between Jupiter and Saturn.
5. _____ The splitting of atoms that releases tremendous amounts of energy is fission.
6. _____ Nitrogen is the most abundant gas in the earth's atmosphere.
7. _____ Tides are caused by the gravitational pull of the earth.
8. _____ The point closest to the sun in the orbit of a planet is aphelion.
9. _____ Petroleum is a form of stored solar energy.
10. _____ A new moon occurs when the earth is between the sun and the moon.

Match these items (each answer, 2 points).
11. _____ Jupiter
12. _____ Mars
13. _____ corona
14. _____ fusion
15. _____ spring tides
16. _____ combustion
17. _____ neap tides
18. _____ photosynthesis
19. _____ Venus
20. _____ nucleus

   a. releases oxygen
   b. low tides
   c. "red planet"
   d. Morning Star
   e. penumbra
   f. fifth planet from sun
   g. center of atom
   h. process of burning
   i. high tides
   j. joining helium and hydrogen nuclei
   k. halo around the sun

Complete these statements (each answer, 3 points).
21. When the moon blocks the sun's light a(n) _____ occurs.
22. In our solar system are two sets of sister planets. One set is Earth and
   a. _____ , and the other set is Uranus and
   b. _____ .
23. The two planets that show phases like the moon are a. _____ and b. _____ .
24. Earth is located between a. _____ and b. _____ .
25. The moon rises and sets fifty minutes _____ each day.
26. The sun's energy is the result of _____ .

27. The position of the sun in the sky determines the _____ of a location.
28. The moon appears to rise in the _____ .
29. We see only one side of the moon because it a. _____ only once while it is making one complete b. _____ .
30. Our solar system consists of _____ planets.

Complete these activities (each numbered item, 5 points).
31. List the planets of our solar system in order from the sun.
    a. _____   e. _____
    b. _____   f. _____
    c. _____   g. _____
    d. _____   h. _____

32. List five theories of how the sun produces solar energy.
    a. _____
    b. _____
    c. _____
    d. _____
    e. _____

33. Make a drawing of a lunar eclipse.

34. Make a drawing of a solar eclipse.

Date _____
Score _____

Science 705 Alternate Test

Name _____

Match these items (each answer, 2 points).

1. _____ precipitation
2. _____ bacteria
3. _____ ozonosphere
4. _____ thermosphere
5. _____ troposphere
6. _____ ozone
7. _____ nitrogen
8. _____ oxygen
9. _____ automobile
10. _____ lungs

a. sphere of overturning
b. most common gas in the atmosphere
c. uncommon form of oxygen
d. where pollutants enter body
e. pollution
f. snow and rain
g. gas necessary for all living things
h. major source of pollution
i. hottest layer of the atmosphere
j. screens out ultraviolet rays
k. necessary organism in nitrogen cycle

Complete these statements (each answer, 3 points).

11. Matthew 7:12 is sometimes called the _____.
12. Two types of air pollutants are a. _____ and
    b. _____ .
13. Bacteria and plants are necessary to complete the _____ cycle.
14. The main thing changing from layer to layer in the atmosphere is the
    _____ .
15. In order for plants to carry on photosynthesis, they must have
    _____ .
16. The probable reason for the increase of carbon dioxide in the
    atmosphere is _____ .
17. The two processes of life involved in the carbon-oxygen cycle are
    a. _____ and b. _____ .
18. The amount of carbon dioxide in the atmosphere is controlled by an
    exchange with the _____ .

Write the letter for the correct answer on each line (each answer, 2 points).

19. The process by which bacteria change nitrogen into nitrogen
    compounds is _____ .
    a. respiration   c. fixation
    b. denitrification   d. photosynthesis
20. The amount of radiation absorbed by the earth _____ the heat lost
    to space.
    a. is greater than   c. is less than
    b. equals   d. reduces
21. Carbon monoxide interferes with the transportation of _____ by the
    blood.
    a. oxygen   c. nitrogen
    b. carbon dioxide   d. hydrogen

22. Sulfur oxides harm the body by _____ .
    a. damaging the lungs
    b. allowing us to catch the flu
    c. keeping the body from making blood
    d. keeping the blood from carrying oxygen
23. In Genesis 1:26 God gave man the responsibility to have _____ over the earth.
    a. pollution   c. ownership
    b. dominion   d. energy

Answer *true* or *false* (each answer, 1 point).
24. _____ The process of changing a gas into a liquid is called evaporation.
25. _____ If man tries hard enough, he can eliminate all pollution.
26. _____ The rate at which oxygen is taken from the atmosphere by living things is equal to the rate at which plants replace it.
27. _____ Clouds reflect 65 percent of the incoming solar radiation.
28. _____ Steel corrodes two to four times faster in cities with many factories polluting the air.
29. _____ Man was given the responsibility to have authority over the entire earth.
30. _____ The trapping of heat by the earth's atmosphere is called the greenhouse effect.

Date _____

Score _____

Name _____

Match these items (each answer, 2 points).

1. _____ weather
2. _____ front
3. _____ humidity
4. _____ bimetallic
5. _____ anemometer
6. _____ wind vane
7. _____ barometer
8. _____ precipitation
9. _____ meteorology
10. _____ wind

a. boundary between two meeting air masses
b. the movement of air over the surface the earth
c. moisture falling from clouds
d. study of the atmosphere
e. the amount of moisture present in the atmosphere
f. the state of the atmosphere
g. an instrument for measuring wind speed
h. an instrument for determining air pressure
i. made of two kinds of metal
j. an instrument for determining wind direction

Write the letter of the correct choice (each answer, 2 points).

11. A line connecting points of equal air pressure is a/an _____ .
   a. isotherm   c. wind
   b. isobar   d. cyclone

12. Clouds that occur in broad layers are _____ .
   a. cirrus   c. nimbo
   b. cumulus   d. stratus

13. The clouds that are made of many tiny ice crystals are _____ .
   a. cirrus   c. nimbo
   b. cumulus   d. stratus

14. Amateurs can forecast weather if they observe barometer readings, wind directions, and _____ .
   a. precipitation   c. humidity
   b. temperature   d. cloud formation

15. Weather sayings about wind, clouds, and barometers are _____ .
   a. useful   c. superstition
   b. unscientific   d. useless

16. As air is warmed it _____ .
   a. sinks   c. rises
   b. evaporates   d. boils

17. A hurricane will die out when it _____ .
   a. reaches land   c. changes to snow
   b. begins raining   d. reaches the equator

18.   The most useful tool the meteorologist has in forecasting the weather is the _____.
     a. weather balloon   c. weather satellite
     b. weather map   d. weatherman

19.   A boundary between two air masses that is not moving is a _____.
     a. occluded front   c. stationary front
     b. cyclonic front   d. warm front

20.   The air movement around a high is _____.
     a. low   c. windy
     b. counterclockwise   d. clockwise

Answer *true* or *false* (each answer, 1 point).

21.   _____   Groundhog Day as a means of predicting weather is superstition.

22.   _____   Before weather information can be sent out, it must be changed into a code.

23.   _____   A cold front forms when warm air begins pushing colder air.

24.   _____   The center low-pressure area of a hurricane is called a cyclone.

25.   _____   A southwest wind and a rising barometer indicate fair weather.

Complete these statements (each answer, 3 points).

26.   The temperature to which the air must be cooled to become saturated with water vapor is _____.

27.   A cold, dry air mass forming over land near the poles is called

_____.

28.   The tendency of a moving object to curve due to the rotation of the earth is the _____.

29.   Precipitation covering a large area ahead of the front is typical of a/an _____ front.

30.   Tornadoes that occur over the ocean are called _____.

Answer these questions (each numbered item, 5 points).

31. What are four sources of weather information the National Weather Service receives?

    a. _____

    b. _____

    c. _____

    d. _____

32. What are the three basic types of clouds?

    a. _____

    b. _____

    c. _____

Date _____

Score _____

Name _____

Match these items (each answer, 2 points)
1. _____ jungle
2. _____ Gobi
3. _____ nomadic
4. _____ steppes
5. _____ Mediterranean climate
6. _____ Pygmy
7. _____ doldrums
8. _____ tree line
9. _____ Australia
10. _____ permafrost

a. an African of small stature
b. ocean regions near the equator
c. wandering desert tribesman
d. deeply frozen earth
e. wet winters, dry summers
f. urban areas
g. plains
h. a large desert in Asia
i. a rain forest of small trees, bushes, and vines
j. its center is a large, desert area
k. the point above which trees do not grow

Write the letter for the correct choice on each line (each answer, 2 points).
11. Precipitation composed of lumps of ice is called _____.
   a. hail   b. sleet   c. snow
12. Pygmies use primitive weapons such as _____.
   a. muskets   b. harpoons   c. poisoned arrows
13. The Eskimos earn money mainly by _____.
   a. flying   b. fishing   c. fur trading
14. The population of a steppe community is mostly engaged in _____.
   a. governing   b. farming   c. trading
15. The climate to the east of a mountain range is usually very _____.
   a. dry   b. cold   c. wet
16. Temperatures near the equator are usually _____.
   a. somewhat warm   b. very warm   c. freezing
17. Almost all of northern Africa is occupied by _____.
   a. the Sahara Desert   b. the Great Oasis   c. permafrost
18. The equator is a latitude of _____.
   a. 0°   b. 60°   c. 90°
19. The _____ is an ocean current bringing cool air from the north.
   a. North Atlantic Drift   b. Labrador Current   c. Gulf Stream
20. The condition of the air over a region averaged through a period of years is _____.
   a. weather   b. climate   c. air pressure

65

Answer *true* or *false* (each answer, 1 point)

21. _____ Antarctica has a polar climate.
22. _____ Above the Arctic Circle the sun is almost directly overhead.
23. _____ Climate is the day-to-day changes in the air.
24. _____ Normal sea level air pressure is 14.7 pounds per square foot.
25. _____ The camel is the mainstay of most Bedouins.
26. _____ Eskimos live mainly in wooden shacks.
27. _____ Winds are turned to the right in the Northern Hemisphere.
28. _____ Mountainous areas have little or no rainfall.
29. _____ Places having equal temperatures are joined by isotherms on weather maps.
30. _____ In the humid subtropics the temperatures can drop below freezing.

Complete these activities (each numbered item, 5 points).

31. List the four parts of climate.

a. _____

b. _____

c. _____

d. _____

32. Name the type of climate you live in and explain your answer.

_____

_____

_____

48 / 60

Date _____

Score _____

Name _____

Answer *true* or *false* (each answer, 1 point).
1. _____ The nucleus is the outside of the cell.
2. _____ All muscles are voluntary.
3. _____ Your tongue has about 3,000 taste buds.
4. _____ The cerebrum controls intelligence.
5. _____ Excretion means *take in*.
6. _____ The center of a bone is bone marrow.
7. _____ Two or more tissues work together to form a cell.
8. _____ The cerebellum is responsible for all voluntary movement.
9. _____ All messages to your brain travel through the spinal cord.
10. _____ A synapse is another name for an optical illusion.

Complete these statements (each answer, 3 points).
11. The four tastes are a. _____ , b. _____ ,
     c. _____ , and d. _____ .
12. The idea that all living things are made of cells is part of the

     _____ .
13. The three layers of the skin are a. _____ , b. _____ ,
     and c. _____ .
14. Joints move easily because they are covered with a layer of smooth

     _____ .
15. The part of the eye that closes and opens to let light in is the

     _____ .
16. Something that activates some part of the body is called a

     _____ .
17. The branches of a neuron are called a. _____ and
     b. _____ .

Match these items (each answer, 2 points).
18. _____ middle ear   a. carry neuron message away
19. _____ slide   from the cell
20. _____ involuntary   b. hammer, anvil, and stirrup
21. _____ axons   c. fluid in the cell
22. _____ cytoplasm   d. tendons and cartilage
                                    e. used with a microscope
                                    f. muscle not controlled by will

Complete these activities (each numbered item, 5 points).

23.   Draw and label the three parts of a cell.

24.   List the five senses.

a.   _____

b.   _____

c.   _____

d.   _____

e.   _____

25.   Draw and label a neuron.

59 / 74

Date   _____

Score   _____

Name _____

Match these items (each answer, 2 points).

1. _____ thyroid   a. the throat structure not
              used in breathing
2. _____ hemoglobin   b. controls all growth
3. _____ enamel   c. take blood from the heart
4. _____ pituitary   d. removes dust from the air
              you breath
5. _____ larynx   e. main function of the
              bladder
6. _____ vein   f. controls the thyroid
7. _____ smell   g. regular squeezing
              movement
8. _____ arteries   h. carries oxygen and iron
9. _____ storage   i. brings blood to the heart
10. _____ peristalsis   j. function of the nose
              k. outer covering of the tooth

Answer *true* or *false* (each answer, 1 point).

11. _____ Cilia have no function in the nose.
12. _____ Arteries are the smallest blood vessels in the body.
13. _____ The veins carry blood to the body's organs.
14. _____ The lungs work closely with the heart.
15. _____ The human body has one adrenal gland.
16. _____ The bladder walls are stiff.
17. _____ Metabolism is the rate at which your body burns food.
18. _____ The larynx is called the voice box.
19. _____ Teeth are made from soft tissue.
20. _____ The kidneys prevent your body from losing too much water,
sugar, or salt by reclaiming some materials.

Complete these statements (each answer, 3 points).

21. The funnel-shaped part of the kidney is the _____ .
22. When muscles relax, the blood in the veins does not flow backwards
because of the veins' _____ .
23. The nose is divided into two parts by the _____ .
24. Blood leaves the heart through _____ .
25. The tiny projections in the small intestine responsible for absorption are
called _____ .
26. If food goes down the windpipe, you start coughing and choking to
keep food from reaching the _____ .
27. The pituitary gland is divided into the a. _____ and
b. _____ .
28. The heart and lungs work together to carry oxygen to every
_____ .

In the blank next to each item write the system to which it belongs; respiratory, circulatory, digestive, excretory, and endocrine (each answer, 3 points).

29. platelets   _____
30. kidney   _____
31. large intestine _____
32. heart   _____
33. adrenal   _____

Complete these activities (each numbered item, 5 points).

34. List the three types of cells in the blood.

   a. _____

   b. _____

   c. _____

35. Explain why food goes down the esophagus and not down the trachea.

   _____

   _____

   _____

66 / 82

Date _____

Score _____

Name _____

Match these items (each answer, 2 points).

1. _____	meter	a.	standard unit of volume
2. _____	Newton	b.	"Father of Modern Science"
3. _____	meteor	c.	patterns of stars
4. _____	cirrus	d.	brightest star in the sky
5. _____	skeleton	e.	puffy clouds
6. _____	Galileo	f.	cells grouped together
7. _____	liter	g.	framework of the body
8. _____	Sirius	h.	standard unit of length
9. _____	cumulus	i.	"shooting star"
10. _____	constellation	j.	wispy, thin clouds
		k.	law of universal gravitation

Complete these statements (each answer, 3 points).

11. Breathing out is called _____.
12. Asteroids orbit the sun in space between a. _____ and
    b. _____ .
13. The moon shines at night because it reflects _____ .
14. The abbreviation for a maritime tropical air mass is _____ .
15. The temperature at which air becomes saturated with water is called
    the _____ .

Answer *true* or *false* (each answer, 1 point).

16. _____ The heart and lungs work together to supply oxygen to every cell in the body.
17. _____ The thyroid gland secretes hormones that control water excretion by the kidney.
18. _____ Meteorologists chart warm and cold air masses.
19. _____ Maritime air masses form over land.
20. _____ The test of a hypothesis is called an experiment.
21. _____ The process of taking food into the bloodstream is absorption.
22. _____ The blood vessels that carry blood to the heart are arteries.
23. _____ A circle graph shows the relationship of different parts of the whole.
24. _____ The blood cells that stop bleeding are the red blood cells.
25. _____ Neurons have long branches called axons and dendrites.

Write the letter of the correct choice (each answer, 2 points).

26. The four elements of the weather are temperature, wind, air pressure, and _____ .
   a. clouds   c. tornadoes
   b. fronts   d. precipitation

27. The cold, dry air mass that develops in northern Canada is _____ .
   a. continental tropical   c. maritime polar
   b. continental polar   d. maritime tropical

28. When cold air pushes warmer air the resulting front is called a

   _____ .
   a. occluded front   c. warm front
   b. stationary front   d. cold front

29. Today we know that sun produces energy by _____ .
   a. combustion   c. nuclear fusion
   b. meteor-impact   d. compaction

30. The tiny projections inside the intestines that absorb digested food are the _____ .
   a. villi   c. chyme
   b. alveoli   d. sinuses

31. Digestion begins in the mouth with a digestive juice called _____ .
   a. chyme   c. bacteria
   b. hydrochloric acid   d. saliva

Complete these activities (each numbered item, 5 points.

32. List the four types of air masses.
   a. _____
   b. _____
   c. _____
   d. _____

33. List the three types of blood cells.
   a. _____
   b. _____
   c. _____

56
70

Date _____
Score _____

ANSWER KEYS

SECTION ONE

Answers may vary slightly depending on the resources that are used.

1.1 Fahrenheit was a German physicist who developed the Fahrenheit temperature scale. He made the measurement of temperature more accurate by developing a mercury thermometer.

1.2 Galileo is called the Father of Experimental Science. He discovered the law of the pendulum. He made the first practical use of the telescope in astronomy He built larger and better telescopes.

1.3 Otto von Guericke proved that a vacume could exist. Creating a vacume was foundational for research into electonics and other related new scientific fields.

1.4 Robert Hooke constructed the first reflecting telescope.

1.5 Johannes Kepler was a German astronomer who discovered the three laws of planetary motion. He discovered a better combina tion of lenses for a telescope.

1.6 Anton van Leeuwenhoek was a Dutch scientist who revealed the world of microscopic life through his observations and drawings. He developed a precise grinding process to make high quality lenses.

1.7 Torricelli was an Italian physicist who discovered the principle of the barometer. He invented the mercurial barometer. A barometer is used to measure air pressure.

1.8 Hint:
Discuss the tree's color, height, location, leaf shape and color and taste, bark texture, condition of crumbliness (friability). Discuss the form, color, taste of seeds; attributes of fruits (if present); animal population; parasites (dead or alive). Tell whether the tree is denuded.

1.9 Observations will vary.

1.10 Observations will vary.

1.11 Hint:
Write about the taste and smell of pine needles. Write about the taste and texture of the tree's fruit. Write about the sound and feel of a breaking twig.

1.12 Examples:
How old is the tree?
How many rings does the tree have?
Are there any birds' nests in the tree?
Is the tree climbable?

1.13 Questions will vary.

1.14 observation

1.15 Any order:
a. seeing
b. hearing
c. smelling
d. tasting
e. feeling

1.16 instruments

1.17 Any order:
a. collect accurate data
b. recognize evidence or to think
c. make comparisons

1.18 Either order:
a. observation
b. thinking

1.19 meter

1.20 gram

1.21 liter

1.22 one-millionth

1.23 one-thousandth

1.24 one-hundredth

1.25 one thousand

1.26 An angstrom is one hundred millionth of a centimeter.

1.27 A light year is the distance light travels in a year: almost 6,000,000,000,000 miles or 9,654,000,000,000 meters.

1.28 A micron is one-millionth of a meter.

1.29 Classifications of objects can be made according to color, shape, size, or use of material. Objects belong to the mineral kingdom, the vegetable kingdom, or the animal kingdom.

1.30 Any order:
a. mineral
b. plant or vegetable
c. animal

1.31 a. grow
b. grow and live
c. grow, live, and have feeling

1.32 Similarities   Differences
Examples: Examples:
a. animal   coloring
b. lives in Africa   sound each makes
c. warm-blooded   food each eats

1.33 Classifications will vary.

1.34 Observation will vary: however, observations will describe the differences between a paper clip and a ruler.

1.35 Answers will vary.

1.36 Answers will vary.

1.37 Answers will vary.

1.38 a. observation or question or data or experiments
b. generalization or conclusion

1.39 conservation of matter

1.40 The deductive method of reasoning starts with a general principle that is accepted as true, applies it to a particular case, and arrives at a conclusion. This means the reasoning proceeds from the general to the specific.

1.41 The inductive method of reasoning is one in which one collects many particular cases, finds out what is common, and forms a general rule that is taken to be true. This has the reasoning proceeding from the specific to the general.

1.42 deductive

1.43 deductive

1.44 inductive

1.45 deductive

1.46 inductive

1.47 balance

1.48 Either order:
a. gains
b. loses

1.49 conservation of matter

1.50 inductive

1.51 inductive

1.52 deductive

1.53 Example:
All Christians love God.
Mary is a Christian.
Therefore, Mary loves God.

1.54 Example:
Mary, Joe, Bill, Jan, and Jim are Christians.
Mary, Joe, Bill, Jan, and Jim love God.
Therefore, all Christians love God.

SECTION TWO

2.1   25 years old at least

2.2   The tree rings vary in width due to climate, availability of rainfall, and average temperature.

2.3   The tree rings grew unevenly because of the orientation of the tree and distribution of light in the forest.

2.4   The burn occurred years ago and bark grew over the burn

2.5   Questions will vary.
2.6   Questions will vary.

2.7   Hypotheses will vary, but they must be relevant and reasonable.

2.8   Hypotheses will vary, but they must be relevant and reasonable.

2.9   Hypotheses will vary, but they must be relevant and reasonable.

2.10   Hypotheses will vary, but they must be relevant and reasonable.

2.11   Hypotheses will vary, but they must be relevant and reasonable.

2.12   Hypotheses will vary, but they must be relevant and reasonable

2.13   a. conclusion
       b. information
2.14   Answers will vary.
2.15   Solutions will vary.
2.16   ✔ Drop a ten-pound piece of rubber and a five-pound piece of rubber from 100 feet. Time the fall of each object.

2.17   candle or some other simple flame. something to smother it, matches, flame (candle) holder

2.18   Plans will vary, but you will need a plan which will cut off the oxygen supply.

2.19   This is the step-by-step procedure. Example:
       1. Place pad on table
       2. Put candle (in holder) on pad
       3. Light candle
       4. Place jar over candle
       5. Record observations

2.20   true
2.21   true
2.22   false

2.23   false
2.24   increases

2.25   The clam died.

2.26   January
2.27   fall

2.28   b. 8 in.

2.29   Both lightning and thunder are caused by the same force; or lightning causes thunder.
2.30   Fires need oxygen

2.31   Altitude affects boiling point.

2.32   a. State the problem.
       b. Form hypothesis.
       c. Investigate or experiment.
       d. Interpret data or observation.
       e. Form conclusion.

SECTION THREE

3.1 a. Greek *astron* = star +
        nemein = dictate the laws of
     b. Latin Greek (al) *chemy* = art
        of alloying metals; *-ist* = a
        person who does or makes;
        -iry = occupation or result
     c. Greek *ge* = earth; *logos* =
        word, study
     d. Latin Greek *physis* = nature
3.2 a. Greek *bios* = life; *logos* =
        word or study
     b. Greek *botanikos* or *botane*
        = plant
     c. Greek *oikos* = dwelling;
        logos = word or study
     d. Greek *paleo* or *palaios* =
        ancient; *ontos*, a being;
        logos = word or study
     e. Greek *zoion* = animal;
        logos = word or study
3.3 a. Greek *anthropos* = man; *logos* =
        word, study
     b. Greek *oikos* = house; *nemein* =
        manage or arrange
     c. Greek *ge* = earth; *graphein* =
        write about
     d. Greek *philo* = love; *sophos* =
        wisdom
     e. Greek *psyche* = soul, mind;
        logos = word, study
     f. Latin and Greek *socius* =
        companion; *logos* = word, study
3.4 a. Greek *logos* = word or study
     b. Greek *mathema* or *manthanein* =
        science, to learn; *techne* =
        art, method, system
3.5-3.6 teacher check
3.7-3.10 Any order:
3.7 Astronomy is the study of space.
3.8 Physics is the study of matter
     and energy.
3.9 Chemistry is the study of substances.

3.10 Geology is the study of the
      earth's crust, its layers and
      their history.

3.11-3.14 Any order:
3.11 Zoology is the science that deals
      with animals and animal life.

3.12 Botany is the science that deals
      with plants and plant life.

3.13 Paleontology is a science of the
      forms of life existing in pre-
      historic time as represented by
      fossil animals and plants.

3.14 Ecology is a science that studies
      the effect of the environment
      upon animals and plants.
3.15-3.20 Any order:
3.15 Sociology is the study of the
      nature, origin, and development
      of human society and community life.
3.16 Psychology is the science of the
      study of the mind.
3.17 Anthropology is the science of
      man dealing with his physical
      characteristics, the development
      of races, and the cultures, cus-
      toms, and beliefs of mankind.
3.18 Economics is the science of pro-
      duction, distribution, and consump-
      tion of goods and services.
3.19 Philosophy is the study of the truth or
      principles underlying all real knowledge.
3.20 Geography is a study of the earth's
      surface, climate, continents, coun-
      tries, peoples, industries, and
      products.
          3.21-3.22 Any order:
3.21 Mathematics is the process of
3.22 Logic is the process of thinking.

SECTION FOUR

4.1 Either order:
   a. A theoretical scientist uses his mind to understand scientific principles.
   b. An experimental scientist proves or disproves theories through testing.

4.2 Engineers are called *applied scientists* because engineers apply the principles of science to the needs of mankind.

4.3 A technician assists engineers and scientists in operating equipment and collecting data.

4.4 Either order:
   a. The teacher directs the learning process.
   b. The teacher interprets complex, unfamiliar ideas and translates them into understandable language.

4.5 Any order:
   a. teaching
   b. government
   c. private industry, medicine, dentistry, etc.

4.6 Job descriptions will vary

4.7 Graph

4.8 Graph

SECTION ONE

1.1 Any order:
   a. length
   b. temperature
   c. time
   d. mass

1.2 metric

1.3 a. metron   b. measurement

1.4 a. 1792- The United States adopted a system of decimal currency.
   b. 1821- President John Quincy Adams asked Congress to adopt the metric system.
   c. 1866- Congress made metric units legal.
   d. 1968- Congress authorized study of metrics.
   e. 1975- President Gerald Ford signed Metric Conversion Act.

1.5 Any order:
   a. Follows decimal system
   Example: 10 millimeters- 1 centimeter
   b. Uses standard prefixes
   Example: millimeter, milliliter, milligram
   c. Has a single basic unit for length, another for volume, another for mass, and so on.
   Example: liter compared to tsp., tbsp., cup, pt., qt., gal.
   d. Computations are easier.
   Example: 2.45 m + 3.67 m = 6.12 m

1.6 a. Example: I would use a paper clip. I would draw a line the same length as my pencil. Then I would see how many times the paper clip fit along the line. That process tells how many paper clips long my pencil is.
   b. Example: I would use my pencil to measure my desk. I would see how many times my pencil fit across my desk. That tells me how many pencil widths my desk is.

1.7 teacher check

1.8 a. 4 cm
   b. 2 cm
   c. 8 cm

1.9 1

1.10 1

1.11 700

1.12 700

1.13 397 cents

1.14 3.97 m or 397 cm

1.15 6 dollars 97 cents or 697 cents

1.16 6 m 97 cm or 697 cm

1.17 Example: 3 to 4 m

1.18 Example: approximately 250 cm

1.19 Widths will vary.

1.20 Lengths will vary.

1.21 1

1.22 3

1.23 5000

1.24 2000

1.25 1

1.26 4

1.27 7000

1.28 9000

1.29 552

1.30 368

1.31 224

1.32 1,554

1.33 teacher check

1.34 teacher check

1.35 Examples:
  a. teacher-desk width, chair back height, rib height
  b. height of basketball hoop, school-hall width, Alaskan brown bear
  c. length of an automobile, common room length, football field striping

1.36 Examples:
  a. paper clip, coin thickness, movie film width
  b. room dimensions, track and field events, wave length
  c. distance between cities, auto race course, distance across continents

1.37 a. A miss is as good as a mile.
  b. Give him an inch; he'll take a yard.
  c. He is just inching along.

1.38 Measurements will vary.

1.39 An average is a better estimate of the true measurement than is just one reading.

1.40 8

1.41 18

1.42 Example:
  I will use a meter stick. I will find how many meters fit along the length and along the width. I will multiply the L x W.

1.43-1.48: approximate measurements

1.43 12 cm²

1.44 10 cm²

1.45 12 m²

1.46 20 m²

1.47 15 m²

1.48 12 m²

1.49 approximately 4-5 cm²

1.50 approximately 144 cm²-240 cm²

1.51 approximately 600 cm²

1.52 approximately 2-4 m²

1.53 Activity A:
  Yes, an average is more reliable.
  Activity B:
  a. 36 cm x 1 cm
     18 cm x 2 cm
     12 cm x 3 cm
     9 cm x 4 cm
     6 cm x 6 cm
  Activity B:
  b. 40 cm x 1 cm
     20 cm x 2 cm
     10 cm x 4 cm
     8 cm x 5 cm
  c. factors of 60, 72, and 96 six rectangles for each of the three numbers
  Activity C:
  teacher check

1.54 Definitions will vary.

1.55 1

1.56 3

1.57 2,000

1.58 6

1.59 3; 824

1.60 2; 486

1.61 6.481

1.62 4.592

1.63 a. no
  b. rock displaces water
  c. They should be the same.
  d. no

1.64 48 cm³

1.65 24 cm³

1.66 Classifications will vary.

1.67 a. 300 ml
  b. 7,200 ml or 7.2 L

1.68 Tables will vary.

1 tsp.	=	5 ml
1 tbsp.	=	15 ml
1 cup	=	236 ml
1 pint	=	473 ml
1 quart	=	946 ml
1 gallon	=	$3\frac{8}{10}$ L

1.69   Mass is the measure of matter in an object. It is measured on a balance and is the same everywhere.

1.70   Gravity is the force that pulls all objects toward the center of the earth.

1.71   Weight is the measure of the pull of gravity. It is measured with a spring scale and becomes less as the object moves away from the earth.

1.72   kilogram

1.73   Example:
I will use paper clips as my standard. I will put the object on one end of the balance. I will add paper clips until the balance is even. Then I will count the paper clips.

1.74   1

1.75   1

1.76   500

1.77   300
1.78   750
1.79   690
1.80   3
1.81   8
1.82   3.7
1.83   5
1.84   9,000
1.85   2
1.86   helper check
1.87   Examples will vary.
1.88   Examples will vary.
1.89   Examples will vary.
1.90   Examples will vary.
1.91   Examples will vary.
1.92   Examples will vary.

SECTION TWO

2.1   13
2.2   Big Bear
2.3   Little Bear
2.4   13
2.5   26

2.6

M = Mercury   Ms = Mars   U = Uranus
V = Venus   J = Jupiter N = Neptune
E = Earth   S = Saturn

2.7

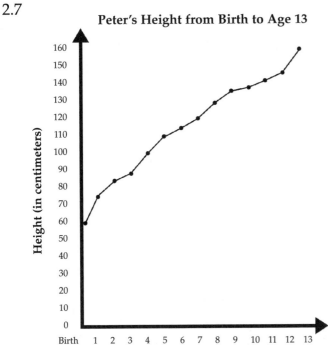

Peter's Height from Birth to Age 13

Height (in centimeters)

160
150
140
130
120
110
100
90
80
70
60
50
40
30
20
10
0

Birth 1 2 3 4 5 6 7 8 9 10 11 12 13

Peter's Age

2.8 Any order:
a. Present information
b. Show relationships
c. Catch reader's attention
d. Provide easily available information

2.9 Any order:
a. bar
b. line
c. pictograph
d. circle

2.10 Precision is lost. We cannot be sure we are plotting or reading the exact figure. The space between data points is not precise.

2.11 a. _x_ Peter
b. _x_ China
c. _x_ The Bible
d. _x_ Susan

2.12 Number of People Who Speak Each of Eight Languages

2.13 100,000,000

2.14 20,000,000

2.15 English

2.16 60,000,000

2.17 French or Portuguese

2.18

Kindergarten

Grade 1

Grade 2

Grade 3

Grade 4

Grade 5

Grade 6

Grade 7

Grade 8

Each Figure Represents 10 Students

2.19 Regional Distribution of Black Population-1860 and 1960

2.20 The chart tells what the actual black population is and the percent of the total population that is black.

2.21 West, North Central, and Northeast

2.22 Examples:
The South is losing blacks.
The greatest increases in black population were in the North East and North Central regions.

2.23

Recreation 30%

Missions 6.7%

Tithe 10%

School Supplies 13.3%

Savings 40%

83

SECTION ONE

1.1 Any order:
a. Most stars rise in the east, set in west.
b. Sun and moon rise in east, set in west
c. Sun rises and sets farther north in summer; farther south in winter.
d. Moon does not always rise at the same time.

1.2 Any order:
a. the sun and stars – day and night
b. the motion of the moon – month
c. the motion of sun against the stars – year and seasons

1.3 Either order:
a. stars were guideposts for travelers
b. stars helped man tell time

1.4 Example: "The heavens declare the glory of God; and the firmament sheweth his handiwork."

1.5 teacher check

1.6 position of stars changes

1.7 $186,000 \frac{mi.}{sec.} \times 60 \frac{sec.}{min.} \times 60 \frac{mi.}{hr.} \times 24 \frac{hr.}{day} \times$

$365 \frac{day}{year} = 5,865,696,000,000 \frac{mi.}{year}$

1.8 nine years from now

1.9 Light leaving the star now will take nine years to travel through space to earth.

1.10 teacher check

1.11 Sequence of answers may start anywhere.

Column 1:	Column 2:
The Fishes	The Ram
The Ram	The Bull
The Bull	The Twins
The Twins	The Crab
The Crab	The Lion
The Lion	The Maiden
The Maiden	The Scales
The Scales	The Scorpion
The Scorpion	The Archer
The Archer	The Goat
The Goat	The Water Carrier
The Water Carrier	The Fishes

1.12 teacher check

1.13 figure with head, arms, chest of a man and legs of a horse

1.14 a legend or story

1.15 lasting through the whole year

1.16 a pattern of stars

1.17 Any three:
Orion, Pleiades, Gemini, Taurus, Canis Major and Canis Minor

1.18 Altair, Vega, Deneb

1.19 all stars seen would be circumpolar

1.20 no stars seen would be circumpolar

1.21 Proxima Centauri, $4\frac{3}{10}$ light years

1.22 sun

1.23 teacher check

1.24 teacher check

1.25 Both have earth at center, sun between Venus and Mars, fixed stars on one sphere and a Prime Mover. Ptolemy used epicycles to explain retrograde motion of planets. They made circles on circles with earth as center.

1.26
a. when it is on the outside of your friend's circle
b. when it passes between you and friend
c. ball turning between you and friend appears to be moving backward as you watch friend
d. when it passes directly between you and friend

1.27
a. it would appear to move backward between earth and the line of its orbit
b. at times they would be closer than at other times

1.28 student drawing like Figure 5

1.29 a. mass of rock or metal traveling through space
  b. mass of rock or metal that enters earth's atmosphere from space
  c. rock or metal that has reached earth from space

1.30 a. having to do with meteors
  b. having to do with meteorites

1.31 a. ° (circle 1 mm diameter)
  b. 100

1.32 metallic

1.33 (Optional activity) teacher check

SECTION TWO

2.1 answers may vary

2.2 a. no
  b. They would have to travel together. One couldn't get ahead of or behind the other.

2.3 more complicated one

2.4 Circles within circles are more complicated than circles.

2.5 Complicated answers do not fit nature and are not usually accurate.

2.6 Any order:
  a. position of moon changes from night to night
  b. sun is eclipsed and moon is eclipsed
  c. planets do not move like stars do

2.7 We cannot feel the earth moving, but we can see the sun, moon, and stars "move."

2.8 Ptolemy requires epicycles to explain motions of planets. According to Copernicus, all the planets have the same motion.

2.9 Any order:
  a. Earth is not the center of the universe.
  b. Planets revolve around the sun and the sun is center of the solar system.
  c. Apparent motion of the sun is explained by the real motion of the earth.

2.10 Osiander's preface said Copernicus' cosmology was a method for calculating motions and not to be taken seriously.

2.11 Any order:
  a. earth wobbles
  b. route of earth around sun
  c. length of year to within 28 seconds
  d. diagrammed planets in correct order and determined approximate period of revolution
  e. recognized basic principle of relativity

2.12 teacher check

2.13 same size but clearer

2.14 the longer the tube the larger the image

2.15 to increase size of image

2.16 smaller inverted image

2.17 Galileo was convinced that you must observe *how* it happens before explaining what happens.

2.18 more interested in "what"; not interested in making observations – just thinking

2.19 Galileo's refracting telescope used lenses; it was subject to blurring by aberration. Newton's reflecting telescope was shorter, but did not have the problem of blurring.

2.20 by placing a small mirror at 45° angle inside to reflect the image to the eyepiece

2.21 extremely careful observations over many years

2.22 Both believed the sun revolved around the earth.

2.23 He made very careful nightly observations that were later used in explaining the heavens.

2.24 The earth was the center (Ptolemy). All other planets revolved around sun (Copernicus).

2.25 He relied on Aristotle's theory that the orbits were perfect circles.

2.26 The ellipse becomes more circular.

2.27 no

2.28 having or representing the sun as the center

2.29 the point in a planet's orbit that is farthest from the sun

2.30 the point in a planet's orbit that is nearest the sun

2.31 teacher check

2.32 He built on the work of all the other great scientists.

2.33 The Greeks looked for the *why* of happenings. They depended on reasoning. Newton experimented and observed, trying to uncover the *how* of events.

2.34 Any order:
a. every object pulls every other object
b. gravitational pull depends on mass
c. gravitational pull depends on distance between the two objects

2.35 Both the cow and the earth have mass and therefore attract other objects.

2.36 North Pole

2.37 Equator

2.38 North Pole

2.39 Equator

2.40 no

2.41 The part of the sky you see is defined by your horizon. As your horizon changes, the part of the sky you see changes.

2.42 a. Sun would cross zenith at noon.
b. Sun would be halfway between highest and lowest altitude in sky at noon.
c. Sun would be just rising to begin a six-month long day.

2.43 to measure altitude accurately

2.44 true north is the reference point to measure azimuth accurately

2.45 answers will vary

2.46 teacher check

2.47 astrolabe not level, astrolabe not lined to true north, inaccurate reading

2.48 INSTRUMENT, DATE OF INVENTION, NATION
refracting telescope, 1608-1609, Holland – Italy
reflecting telescope, 1669, England
astrolabe, 150 B.C., Greece
camera, 11th century, Europe
radio telescope, 1931, United States
spectroscope, 1860, Germany

2.49 to bend, as light passing through a lens

2.50 energy that is transmitted in the form of light, x rays, radio waves, and so on

SECTION ONE

1.1 Any order:
  a. heat energy
  b. light energy
  c. photosynthesis
  d. comfortable temperature
     for man

1.2 teacher check

1.3 teacher check

1.4 false

1.5 false

1.6 true

1.7 true

1.8 false

1.9 a

1.10 a

1.11 c

1.12 Any order:
  a. Combustion – hydrogen and
     oxygen on the sun combine
     to give off energy
  b. Contraction – gravitation com-
     presses gases to generate
     energy
  c. Meteor – meteors falling into
     sun emitted energy
  d. Radioactivity – radioactive
     substances on the sun emit
     energy
  e. Carbon cycle – four hydrogen
     fuse to form one helium in
     the presence of carbon acting
     as a catalyst or
     Nuclear fusion – energy is
     released when hydrogen nuclei
     combine to form helium nuclei

1.13 by splitting the atom

1.14 The sun's energy is created by
     the nuclear fusion of hydrogen
     nuclei to form helium nuclei.

1.15 one-two millionth

1.16 70 percent

SECTION TWO

2.1 Mercury
2.2 Mercury
2.3 fifty-nine days
2.4 eighty-eight days
2.5 the gravity
2.6 0.38
2.7 0.05 or 1/20
2.8 data table
2.9 Either order:
  a. Mercury
  b. Earth
2.10 108,230,000
2.11 phases
2.12 243 days

2.13 225 days
2.14 0.88
2.15 0.82
2.16 clouds do not change shape
2.17 data table
2.18 false
2.19 false
2.20 true
2.21 true
2.22 true
2.23 data table
2.24 data table
2.25 red color

2.26   228,000,000 km
2.27   687
2.28   24 hours 37 minutes

2.29   Either order:
       a. Phobos
       b. Deimos

2.30   0.39
2.31   0.11
2.32   revealed meteor craters; photo-
       graphed both moons, surface details,
       and a dust storm
2.33   a. no
       b. highs are never above
           freezing
2.34   receives less than half heat
       and light, smaller than earth,
       less gravity, landscape is cratered

2.35   gravitational

2.36   Dark areas that appeared to be
       oceans; changes in landscape;
       apparent canals.

2.37   Hint:
       include information about
       temperature, atmosphere, surface
       gravity, distance (time to
       get there)

2.38   largest
2.39   778,400,000
2.40   318.3
2.41   2.64
2.42   9 hours 55 minutes

2.43   twelve years

2.44   a. four
       b. sixteen
2.45   red spot
2.46   Example:
       Jupiter's red spot is three times
       the diameter of the earth. The

2.46   cont.
       red spot was first seen in
       1875 and has become fainter every year.
2.47   Hints for information to
       include in paragraph:
       measured radiation belts, reported
       amounts of hydrogen and helium,
       photographs of polar regions, new
       data on red spot, magnetic field,
       temperature
2.48   data table
2.49   1,424,600,000 km
2.50   a little more than ten hours
2.51   29.5 years
2.52   1.17
2.53   95.3
2.54   its rings
2.55   twenty-three
2.56   Saturn's rings consist of thousands
       of narrow ringlets. These ringlets
       are made up of billions of ice
       particles that vary in size. The
       rings surround the equator of the
       planet. The rings are thin, measur-
       ing only 16 km in thickness.
2.57   Saturn is too far away. The
       trip would take at least five
       years. It is too difficult
       to equip a spaceship with
       power for that period of time.
       It would be too far from the sun
       to use solar energy.
2.58   data table
2.59   2,866,900,000 km
2.60   14.7
2.61   0.92
2.62   Sir William Herschel
2.63   North Pole faces sun for twenty
       years; then South Pole faces
       sun for twenty years. Rotation
       is clockwise.
2.64   Orbit around sun was not as
       expected; Astronomers deduced
       that another undiscovered
       planet must be pulling on it.
2.65   data table

2.66   4,486,100,000 km

2.67   about every 16 hours

2.68   165 years

2.69   Johann Galle

2.70   17.3

2.71   1.23

2.72   Neptune is slightly larger
       and colder— appears bluish;
       Uranus appears greenish

2.73   a. no
       b. Uranus still did not behave
           according to established
           laws. Still another
           planet had to be undiscovered.

2.74   data table

2.75   5,890,000,000

2.76   6 days 9 hours

2.77   248 years

2.78   the same as earth

2.79   0.15

2.80   Percival Lowell

2.81   it is so far away

2.82   data table

2.83   c

2.84   a

2.85   c

2.86   b

2.87   d

2.88   Asteroids (planetoids) are
       masses of rock orbiting the sun.
       They are between Mars and Jupiter.
       They shine with reflected sun-
       light and range in size from less
       than one km to 800 km.

2.89   Comets are made of frozen gases and
       dirt. They travel in elongated ellip-
       tical orbits around the sun. Gases
       form the tail, which is always
       pushed away from the sun. They con-
       tinuously lose some of their material
       and will vanish, leaving particles
       of dust that may enter the earth's
       atmosphere as meteors.

2.90   1.2 cm

2.91   1.3 cm

2.92   0.7 cm

2.93   14.3 cm

2.94   12.0 cm

2.95   5.1 cm

2.96   4.9 cm

2.97   0.3 cm

2.98   Multiply your weight by the
       surface gravity factor for
       each celestial body.

2.99   0.38, teacher check

2.100 0.39, teacher check

2.101 2.64, teacher check

2.102 1.17, teacher check

2.103 0.92, teacher check

2.104 1.23, teacher check

2.105 0.15, teacher check

2.106 0.16, teacher check

2.107 a. 57,900,000
       b. 4,878
       c. 88 days
       d. 59 days
       e. 0.05
       f. 0.38
       g. 0

2.108 a. 108,230,000
     b. 12,100
     c. 225 days
     d. 243 days
     e. 0.82
     f. 0.88
     g. 0

2.109 a. 150,000,000
     b. 13,000
     c. 365.25 days
     d. 23 hours 56 minutes
     e. 1.00
     f. 1.00
     g. 1

2.110 a. 228,000,000
     b. 6,791
     c. 687 days
     d. 24 hours 37 minutes
     e. 0.11
     f. 0.39
     g. 2

2.111 a. 778,400,000
     b. 142,700
     c. 12 years
     d. 9 hours 55 minutes
     e. 318.3
     f. 2.64
     g. 16

2.112 a. 1,424,600,000
     b. 120,000
     c. 29.5 years
     d. 10+ hours

     e. 95.3
     f. 1.17
     g 23

2.113 a. 2,866,900,000
     b. 50,800
     c. 84 years
     d. 17 hours
     e. 14.7
     f. 0.92
     g. 15

2.114 a. 4,486,100,000
     b. 48,600
     c. 165 years
     d. about 16 hours
     e. 17.3
     f. 1.23
     g. 2

2.115 a. 5,890,000,000
     b. 3,000
     c. 248 years
     d. 6 days 9 hours
     e. 1.0
     f. 0.15
     g. 1

2.116 a. - -
     b. 3,476
     c. - -
     d. 27 $\frac{1}{3}$ days
     e. - -
     f. 0.16
     g. - -

SECTION THREE

3.1 circular
3.2 circular
3.3 circular
3.4 Example:
    looks like a series of
    half circles up

3.5

3.6 epicycles
3.7 yes
3.8

3.9 a. the earth
    b. moon
    c. sun

3.10 Viewed from the earth, the moon
     moves in a circle. Viewed from
     the sun, the moon moves in epicycles.
3.11 The line describes one-quarter
     of a wavy ellipse around the "sun."

3.12 false
3.13 false
3.14 true
3.15 true
3.16 false
3.17 a. east
    b. west

3.18 of the earth's rotation

3.19 thirteen

3.20 13° or about 50 minutes of time

3.21 50 minutes

3.22 $27\frac{1}{3}$ days

3.23 $29\frac{1}{2}$ days

3.24 because while the moon is revolving around the earth, the earth is revolving around the sun at the rate of 1° per day.

3.25 new moon to new moon ($29\frac{1}{2}$ days)

3.26 daytime

3.27 a. no
b. the lighted side would always be facing the sun—the moon receives its light from the sun.

3.28 The tides are the periodic rise and fall of the level of the ocean.

3.29 gravitational pull of the moon and the sun

3.30 moon

3.31 The same point on earth is directly beneath the moon every 24 hours and 52 minutes. A high tide occurs at that point (nearly) and on the opposite side of the earth.

3.32 moon and sun are in a line and pulling together

3.33 a. tides during full and new moon—highest highs and lowest lows
b. tides during first and third quarters—low high tides and high low tides

3.34 difference between level of water at low tide and level of water at high tide

3.35 one-half of earth would always be day—other half always night

3.36 seasons would not change

3.37 method of telling time by motions in heavens would cease

3.38 lighted side would get very hot— dark side very cold;

3.39 would be pulled to one side of the earth

3.40 could not exist as we know it today

3.41 earth would fall into the sun

SECTION FOUR

4.1 Because the sun, even though larger, is so far away it *appears* to be the same size as the moon.

4.2 a. 384,000 km ÷ 3,476 km = 110.47
b. 152,000,000 km ÷ 1,392,000 km = 109.19
c. If they have the same angular diameters, they must have the same ratio of distance and diameter.

4.3 teacher check

4.4 $6\frac{1}{2}$ cm

4.5 no

4.6 no

4.7 a. no
b. the moon's shadow is cast on only a small portion of the earth's surface

4.8 The moon is far enough away from the earth that the earth's curvature does not block the line of sight.

4.9 The earth must be between the sun and the moon.

4.10 The moon must be between the sun and the earth.

4.11 a. the moon gradually passes into earth's shadow (lunar eclipse)
b. an eclipse of the sun

4.12 See Figure 14 in text.

Science 705 Answer Key

SECTION ONE

1.1 50%

1.2 nitrogen

1.3 oxygen

1.4 water vapor

1.5 Oxygen molecules consist of two oxygen atoms. Ozone molecules are made of three oxygen atoms.

1.6 30 to 60 km above the earth in the ozonosphere

1.7 a region where the concentration of ozone is high.

1.8 temperature

1.9 troposphere

1.10 stratosphere

1.11 mesosphere

1.12 thermosphere

1.13 ionosphere

1.14 b

1.15 c

1.16 a

1.17 b

1.18 a

1.19 troposphere means sphere of overturning

1.20 troposphere

1.21 The top of the stratosphere is warmer than the bottom. Therefore, the cold heavy air is on the bottom.

1.22 Gases in the troposphere, stratosphere, and mesosphere are uniformly mixed. The gases in the thermosphere are found in layers.

1.23 a

1.24 b

1.25 b

1.26 c

1.27 Both layers are warmed from below.

1.28 Gravity arranges the heaviest gases at the bottom and the lightest gases on top.

1.29 It is meaningless because the air is too thin to heat objects passing through it

1.30 a. It is formed when nitrogen and oxygen absorb radiation to become ions.
    b. It is important because it reflects radio waves.

1.31 sun

1.32 a. 30
    b. 30
    c. 40

1.33 Either order:
    a. ionosphere
    b. ozonosphere

1.34 short-wave

1.35 Either order:
    a. carbon dioxide
    b. water vapor

1.36 earth

1.37 night

1.38 a. equator
    b. poles

1.39 The bending of light rays in all directions by gas molecules.

1.40 scattering

1.41 The radiation released by the sun has a shorter wavelength than radiation released by the earth.

1.42 It is the trapping of heat given off by earth after having been heated by the sun. Carbon dioxide and water vapor trap the heat.

1.43 The amount of radiation received by the earth equals the amount of heat lost to space.

1.44 The temperature rose faster in the covered box. (student answers may vary)

1.45 The temperature rose higher in the covered box. (student answers may vary)

1.46 The temperature dropped faster in the uncovered box. (student answer may vary)

1.47 Example:
The plastic or glass acted like carbon dioxide and water vapor in the atmosphere. Sunlight (short waves) can pass through the plastic or glass. Heat (long waves) in the box cannot escape. As a result the temperature rises. In the absence of sunlight the plastic keeps the heat in the box.

1.48 oxygen

1.49 Either order:
a. water
b. carbon dioxide

1.50 energy

1.51 Either order:
a. food
b. oxygen

1.52 ionosphere
1.53 ozonosphere
1.54 burns, cancer, or even death
1.55 thermosphere
1.56 craters
1.57 atmosphere

1.58 Either order:
a. stone
b. metal

1.59 true

1.60 false

1.61 The process by which oxygen combines with food to produce energy.

1.62 The process by which plants use chlorophyll and sunlight to combine carbon dioxide and water to make oxygen and food.

1.63 sunlight, chlorophyll, carbon dioxide, water

1.64 The skin is tanned by small amounts of radiation. Larger amounts can cause the skin to be thin and wrinkled and sometimes cause cancer.

1.65 Radiation shortens the life span.

1.66 bone marrow, sex organs, digestive system, blood vessels

1.67 Atmosphere moderates a planet's temperature: its temperature range is small.

1.68 solid objects moving through space at high speeds

1.69 Meteors (meteoroids in the atmosphere) burn up because they are heated by friction with air molecules.

1.70 Most meteoroids are the size of a grain of sand.

1.71 It is a meteoroid that reaches the earth's surface.

1.72 The atmosphere causes most meteoroids to burn up.

1.73 warming trend
1.74 cool
1.75 true
1.76 More carbon dioxide will trap more heat (the greenhouse effect) and raise temperatures on earth.

1.77 The burning of fossil fuels adds carbon dioxide to the atmosphere.

1.78 They give off carbon dioxide and water vapor.

1.79 Example:
Temperatures could become warmer over the entire earth. Warmer temperatures might melt the ice caps and glaciers, raising the ocean levels.

SECTION TWO

2.1   c

2.2   e
2.3   a or b
2.4   b or a
2.5   d
2.6   a
2.7   c
2.8   a
2.9   b
2.10   c
2.11   water droplets

2.12   clouds

2.13   more

2.14   rivers and streams
2.15   They all involve materials essential for life and they all require the atmosphere to complete the cycle.
2.16   oceans, streams, rivers, lakes, soil, plants, animals
2.17   Plants draw up moisture and evaporate (transpire) some of it. Some may seep into rivers. Some seeps through rock layers back to the sea.
2.18   Rain is formed by water vapor condensing on dust in the air. When the water droplets are large enough, they fall from the clouds.
2.19   Snow forms when water vapor condenses below the freezing point.
2.20   Some water is trapped in snow or ice for many years.
2.21   Example:
Kansas City receives 36 inches per year, more than the average
2.22   Student answer will read either increased or decreased.

2.23   If 2.22 was increased, the precipitation was greater. If 2.22 was decreased, the evaporation was greater
2.24   c
2.25   a
2.26   b
2.27   true
2.28   true
2.29   true
2.30   false
2.31   true
2.32   Either order:
     a. photosynthesis
     b. respiration
2.33   equals

2.34   a

2.35   c
2.36   Any order:
oceans, rocks, and living things

2.37   The oceans would absorb some of the carbon dioxide from the atmosphere.
2.38   The oceans would release some of the carbon dioxide to the atmosphere.

2.39   Photosynthesis changes carbon dioxide into oxygen and food containing carbon.
2.40   Respiration changes oxygen and food containing carbon into carbon dioxide.
2.41   The oxygen supply would run out in 2,000 years.

2.42   pressure and no oxygen
243   false

2.44   false
2.45   true

2.46 true

2.47 false

2.48 Either order:
   a. plants
   b. bacteria

2.49 nitrogen compounds

2.50 Either order:
   a. soil
   b. roots of legumes

2.51 plant protein

2.52 ammonia

2.53 artificial fertilizer

2.54 Nitrogen is a component in many different compounds. It can release energy when changing from one compound to another.

2.55 lightning and blue-green algae

2.56 Bacteria use food provided by plants as energy to change nitrogen into nitrates.

2.57 He can plant legumes like clover, peas, or alfalfa and plow them into the soil at the end of the growing season.

2.58 They must eat plants or other animals.

2.59 Denitrification is the process by which nitrogen is released from nitrogen compounds by special bacteria.

2.60 Bacteria can release nitrogen from ammonia or change ammonia into nitrates.

SECTION THREE

3.1 a

3.2 c

3.3 b

3.4 a

3.5 d

3.6 c

3.7 b

3.8 a

3.9 a

3.10 waste substances, not ordinarily found in the atmosphere, that interfere with natural cycles

3.11 Either order:
   a. settling out
   b. rain or snow

3.12 carbon monoxide

3.13 ability of blood to transport oxygen

3.14 false

3.15 false

3.16 true

3.17 automobiles, electric power plants, factories, home furnaces, and burning dumps

3.18 particles and gases

3.19 Example:
The exhaust from cars could be cooled slowly to allow the nitrogen oxides to break apart.

3.20 a

3.21 c

3.22 c

3.23 a

3.24 lungs (or) nose

3.25 lungs

3.26 electric power plants and automobiles

3.27 life span or life expectancy

3.28 Interferes with the blood's ability to carry oxygen. Dulls the senses, causing people to be prone to accidents.

3.29 smog and sulfur oxides

3.30 Damage to the lungs causes the heart to work harder.

3.31 warm air layer over a cool air layer can act like a lid holding pollution in the valley

3.32 b

3.33 c

3.34 d

3.35 a

3.36 dominion

3.37 rule or authority

3.38 man

3.39 false

3.40 false

3.41 Because God created the earth, He also knows the best way to enjoy the earth.

3.42 He is responsible for protecting his country and developing its resources.

3.43 The resources will be wasted and will run out. Pollution will become worse.

3.44 Matthew 7:12: The golden rule.

3.45 The Clean Air Act was passed. States have passed their own laws to control pollution.

3.46 It gives a reason for man to control pollution, by imposing penalties.

3.47 How much are we willing to pay to control pollution? What are we willing to do without to control pollution? How much pollution are we willing to accept?

3.48 teacher check

SECTION ONE

1.1   b

1.2   a

1.3   c

1.4   d

1.5   a

1.6   b

1.7   c

1.8   a

1.9   Either order:
    a. Fahrenheit
    b. Celsius

1.10   a. 32
     b. 0

1.11   a. 212
     b. 100

1.12   Any order:
     a. temperature
     b. pressure
     c. wind
     d. moisture

1.13   The troposphere is heated by the surface of the earth.

1.14   The poles receive less solar radiation because the sun's rays strike at a low angle.

1.15   Heat causes the atoms in an object to move faster.

1.16   Thermometers measure temperature by measuring how much the metal or liquid in the thermometer has expanded.

1.17   Example:
colder temperatures, winds SW-N, decrease in humidity, decreased chance of precipitation

1.18   Example:
warmer temperatures, winds NE-S, increased chance of rain or snow, increase in humidity

1.19   the movement of air over the surface of the earth

1.20   differences in temperature

1.21   a. less dense (lighter)
     b. rises

1.22   a. more dense (heavier)
     b. sinks

1.23   an instrument used to determine wind direction

1.24   an instrument used to measure wind speed

1.25   miles per hour

1.26   a. water
     b. land

1.27   a. vegetation
     b. bare ground

1.28   a. land
     b. water

1.29   A south wind is a wind blowing from the south.

1.30   The winds are named by using both compass points.

1.31   A sea breeze is caused by differences in temperature over land and water during the day and night.

1.32   Example:
A cooler earth would mean less temperature differences and less wind.

1.33   rising

1.34   sinking

1.35   right

1.36 left
1.37 a. west
     b. east
1.38 The general flow is from the poles to the equator.
1.39 The general flow is from the equator to the poles.
1.40 The jet stream is linked to the movement of weather patterns across the earth's surface.
1.41 a ribbon of fast-moving air in the upper troposphere that separates warm air coming from the equator and cold air coming from the poles.
1.42 the tendency of moving objects to curve due to the earth's rotation.
1.43 c
1.44 b
1.45 a
1.46 b

1.47 c

1.48 e
1.49 d

1.50 a
1.51 f
1.52 b
1.53 c
1.54 a
1.55 d
1.56 high
1.57 low
1.58 a. high
     b. low
1.59 a. counterclockwise
     b. inward
1.60 a. clockwise
     b. outward

1.61 A barometer measures pressure by measuring the height from the top of the mercury in the bowl to the top of the mercury in the tube.
1.62 Air pressure becomes less.
1.63 Actual air pressures are converted to sea-level pressure.
1.64 High pressure of sinking air causes warming and evaporation to take place.
1.65 As air gets closer to the center of a low, it rotates faster.
1.66 The rising, expanding, air becomes cooler which favors condensation and the formation of rain clouds.
1.67 A low is maintained by more air rising at the center than is moving in at the sides.
1.68 the amount of water vapor present in the atmosphere.
1.69 air that holds all the water vapor it can possibly hold
1.70 the comparison of the actual amount of water vapor in the air to the maximum amount it can hold expressed as a percent
1.71 the temperature at which the air becomes saturated
1.72 moisture falling from the atmosphere
1.73 false
1.74 true
1.75 false
1.76 Particles of dust, soot, or salt are needed.
1.77 condensation nuclei
1.78 Either order:
     a. Raindrops form by water droplets evaporating and condensing on ice crystals that later melt.
     b. Raindrops form by water droplets capturing other droplets until they are too heavy and fall from clouds.

1.79   rain, snow, sleet, and hail

1.80   Snow is formed when water droplets freeze into ice crystals.

1.81   Sleet is formed when raindrops fall into freezing air.

1.82   Hail is formed by updrafts and downdrafts that alternately freeze raindrops and melt part of them. They grow in size as they pick up more moisture.

1.83   The snow is melted and poured back into the rain gauge.

1.84   Either order:
     a. wet
     b. dry

1.85   rain gauge

1.86   a. ten
     b. twelve

1.87   The can must be shiny to show water droplets that form on the can.

1.88   The ice is added slowly so the dew point is not reached too fast. All the water must be the same temperature.

1.89   The average of many trials is more likely to be closer to the correct value.

1.90   Teacher check – refer to your data chart.

SECTION TWO

2.1   a large body of air having uniform temperature and humidity

2.2   An air mass forms when a large body of air remains in an area long enough to take on the characteristics of the area.

Any order:

2.3   a. continental polar – cP
     b. continental tropical – cT
     c. maritime polar – mP
     d. maritime tropical – mT

2.4   east wind

2.5   continental tropical air mass

2.6   It was formed over the hot, dry desert of Saudi Arabia.

2.7   The Great Lakes are too small and are affected by winds.

2.8   a. dry
      b. over land

2.9   a. wet or moist
      b. over oceans

2.10 a. cold
      b. near the poles or north of the United States

2.11 a. hot
      b. near the equator or south of the United States

2.12 a. cold and dry
      b. northern Canada

2.13 a. hot and dry
      b. northern Mexico

2.14 a. cold and moist
      b. Pacific Ocean off Canada or North Atlantic Ocean

2.15 a. hot and moist
      b. Gulf of Mexico or Pacific Ocean off Mexico

2.16 Example:
      continental polar – Siberia
      maritime tropical – Indian Ocean

2.17 Clouds form when water vapor is cooled below the dew point and condenses on particles as water droplets.

2.18 Cirrus clouds are thin, feathery, and wispy.

2.19 Stratus clouds look like a continuous sheet or layer.

2.20 Stratus clouds form when masses are gently lifted as they move forward.

2.21 Cumulus clouds are puffy clouds.

2.22 Cumulus clouds form when air masses rise vertically.

2.23 c

2.24 d

2.25 b

2.26 a

2.27 Any order:
      a. cirrus
      b. stratus
      c. cumulus

2.28 ice crystals

2.29 seven to ten

2.30 fair weather cumulus

2.31 a stratus-type cloud formed on the ground

2.32 false

2.33 true

2.34 false

2.35 true

2.36 true

2.37 the boundary between two air masses

2.38 a front formed when warm air pushes cold air

2.39 temperature difference

2.40 cirrus

2.41 Rain covers a large area and lasts for one to two days.

2.42 temperature rises, wind changes direction, rain stops, clouds break up

2.43 A front formed when cold air pushes warm air.

2.44 true

2.45 false

2.46 true

2.47 true

2.48 true

2.49 the temperature drops, winds shift to the northwest, air pressure rises, clouds change to fair-weather cumulus.

2.50 the boundary between two cold air masses that have lifted a warm air mass

2.51 closing in

2.52 A cold front catches up with a warm front because the cold front moves faster.

2.53 Weather conditions are a mixture of cold front and warm front.

2.54 a front separating two air masses moving parallel to the front

2.55 warm

2.56 warm

2.57 It may become a warm front or cold front, depending on which air mass begins pushing.

2.58 a small local storm with thunder and lightning

2.59 b

2.60 d

2.61 b

2.62 a

2.63 Either order:
   a. by a cold front
   b. rapid rising of hot air near the ground

2.64 It dies out when all the rain in the cloud has fallen.

2.65 New thunderstorms are formed by the cold air of a downdraft forcing warm, moist air to rise.

2.66 maritime tropical

2.67 one to two hours

2.68 a. April
   b. September

2.69 a narrow, funnel-shaped cloud of rapidly rotating winds

2.70 an announcement that the conditions are right for tornadoes to form and we should watch for them

2.71 an announcement that a tornado has been spotted and that we should take cover.

2.72 a tornado over bodies of water

2.73 b

2.74 a

2.75 a

2.76 a

2.77 b

2.78 d

2.79 The low pressure of a tornado allows the higher pressure inside a building to blow the roofs and walls out.

2.80 National Severe Storms Forecast Center in Kansas City

2.81 A large revolving storm with destructive winds, heavy rains, and high waves and tides.

2.82 The eye of a hurricane is the central low pressure area. It is free of rain and strong winds, and has fewer clouds.

2.83 120

2.84 typhoons

2.85 eighth

2.86 Most hurricanes form over warm oceans between 5° and 20° from the equator.

2.87 A hurricane dies out when it reaches land or colder water.

SECTION THREE

3.1 true

3.2 true

3.3 false

3.4

3.5

3.6

3.7
no movement

3.8 Any order:
   a. weather stations
   b. airplanes
   c. ships
   d. weather balloons
   e. weather satellites
   f. foreign countries

3.9 Weather satellites provide pictures of cloud cover and air masses.

3.10 Weather balloons radio back information about the upper atmosphere.

3.11 a

3.12 c

3.13 God created an orderly world.

3.14 a. 405
    b. 20
    c. 31
    d. .45

3.15 30

3.16 northwest

3.17 a line connecting points on a map that have equal air pressure

3.18 true

3.19 false

3.20 true

3.21 c

3.22 b

3.23 a

3.24 east

3.25 west

3.26 clearing and colder

3.27 rain

3.28 Any order:
    a. lakes
    b. valleys
    c. mountains

3.29 Severe weather occurs when the weather conditions are sharply different on the two sides of the front.

3.30 A meteorologist determines this by tracing the paths of the fronts in the past.

3.31 A passing low in summer brings warmer weather; in winter, colder weather.

3.32 Either order:
    a. short range – for one to two days, very detailed
    b. extended – for five to thirty days, very general, predict only variations from normal

3.33 Any order:
   a. cloud formation
   b. wind direction
   c. barometer reading

3.34 Example:
   rain or snow within twelve to twenty-four hours

3.35 student check

3.36 The two sayings are similar although in different order.
   The red sky is caused by cirrus or stratus clouds ahead of a warm front.

3.37 Red skies in the morning followed by overcast point to the arrival of a warm front and bad weather; the storm will cause high waves.

3.38 No scientific proof exists to back it up.

3.39 Weather sayings based upon clouds, winds, or barometers are usually reliable.

3.40 teacher check

SECTION ONE

1.1 the amount of heat or cold as measured in degrees

1.2 air pressure as measured by a barometer

1.3 a deposit of rain, sleet, snow, ice, or hail

1.4 air in motion

1.5 short

1.6 Either order:
   a. know what to do
   b. know what to wear

1.7 false

1.8 false

1.9 a. cooler

1.10 a. climate

1.11 b. weather

1.12 Any order:
   a. temperature
   b. pressure
   c. wind
   d. precipitation

1.13 radiation

1.14 earth

1.15 more

1.16 14.7 pounds per square inch

1.17 heated (or warmed)

1.18 high

1.19 high

1.20 axis

1.21 c

1.22 f

1.23 b

1.24 e

1.25 d

1.26 Hailstones are formed when tiny ice particles move up and down in a windy cloud gathering more and more ice.

1.27 Teacher check – Example: the rotation of the earth turns the winds to the right in the Northern Hemisphere and to the left in the Southern Hemisphere.

SECTION TWO

2.1-2.6 Any order:

2.1 latitude

2.2 altitude

2.3 nearness to water

2.4 average temperature

2.5 average rainfall

2.6 ocean currents

2.7 horse latitudes

2.8 doldrums

2.9 horse latitudes

2.10 Since the air is heated by the earth, the farther away it is, the less heat it receives.

2.11 Mountains cause clouds to rise, condense, and drop their rain on west slopes. No rain is left to fall east of the mountains.

2.12 Air over land is warmer than air over water. Warm air always rises. When this happens, cooler air from the ocean flows inland.

2.13   The Gulf Stream warms them.
2.14   e
2.15   d
2.16   b
2.17   c
2.18   false
2.19   false
2.20   true
2.21   true

2.22   false
2.23   e
2.24   a
2.25   b
2.26   d
2.27   e
2.28   b
2.29   a
2.30   b

SECTION THREE

3.1   64.4
3.2   rain forests
3.3   jungles

3.4   furniture
3.5   Either order:
       a. rubber
       b. quinine
       or gum, furniture
3.6   summer
3.7   a seasonal wind reversal that
       brings heavy rainfall
3.8   a large farm
3.9   Either order; Examples:
       a. coffee
       b. bananas
3.10   It is less constant because the
       savanna has a dry season each year.
3.11   true

3.12   false
3.13   false
3.14   farther from
3.15   dry

3.16   urban
3.17   mediterranean
3.18   They occur on the west coast and
       in the interior of continents on
       east side of mountain ranges.
3.19   The parched soil is too sun-
       baked to soak up the moisture,
       and it runs off.
3.20   It is a fertile spot in the desert
       where water can be found.
3.21   Nomads usually live in desert areas.
3.22   false
3.23   true
3.24   false
3.25   true
3.26   vertical
3.27   rainfall
3.28   They cause clouds to rise, condense,
       and drop their moisture
3.29   The topsoil and abundant rainfall
       make farming profitable.
3.30   The air is too thin and cold to
       support large plant life.
3.31   false

3.32	true
3.33	true
3.34	f
3.35	a
3.36	g
3.37	b
3.38	h
3.39	d
3.40	e
3.41	generally near the poles
3.42	seven
3.43	Asia
3.44	Siberia
3.45	steppe
3.46	Gobi Desert
3.47	Himalayas
3.48	mediterranean

3.49 a. humid subtropical
       b. cool
3.50 Any order:
       a. Switzerland
       b. France
       c. Germany
       d. Austria
       e. Italy
3.51 polar
3.52 Sahara Desert
3.53 tropical rain forest and savanna
3.54 true
3.55 false
3.56 true
3.57 false
3.58 true
3.59 false
3.60 false
3.61 true
3.62 false

SECTION FOUR

4.1	M
4.2	L
4.3	M
4.4	H, L
4.5	H
4.6	H
4.7	M
4.8	H
4.9	L
4.10	M

4.11 Agriculture is more easily carried on. Machines do much of the work. Jobs take only 8-10 hours per day.
4.12 The cycles of plowing, sowing, and harvesting control life.
4.13 The making of an area into a city and a people into city people.
4.14 Few people in these areas can afford more substantial homes. Permafrost prevents the building of brick or concrete homes in most cases.
4.15 The warmth of the low latitudes makes warm clothing unnecessary; in the high latitudes warm clothing is essential for protection from the weather.

4.16 true

4.17 false

4.18 false

4.19 true

4.20 true

4.21 true

4.22 true

4.23 false

4.24 false

4.25 b

4.26 a

4.27 a

4.28 b

4.29 c

4.30 c

4.31 It provides food, shelter, clothing, transportation, and utensils.

4.32 They would like to steal valuable camels.

4.33 It is thatched, has one door, no windows, and one hole in the roof.

4.34 Any order:
   a. bows and poisoned arrows
   b. fishhooks
   c. spears

4.35 lack of berries and roots to collect

4.36 teacher check

Science 708 Answer Key

SECTION ONE

1.1 Any order:
   a. cell membrane
   b. cytoplasm
   c. nucleus
1.2 false
1.3 true

1.4 true
1.5 false
1.6 Student should see many cells.
Cell membrane and nucleus of
each cell are darker than cytoplasm.
1.7 Probable answer is yes.
1.8 c
1.9 a
1.10 b
1.11 d
1.12 b
1.13 a
1.14 e
1.15 a set of ideas that helps explain
something
1.16 Examples:
theory of relativity,
theory of evolution,
"big bang" theory,
expanding universe theory
1.17 All living things are made of cells.
All life activities are done by
cells.
1.18 absorption: to take in
   excretion: to send out

1.19 Either order:
   a. excretion
   b. absorption
1.20 Either order:
   a. RNA
   b. DNA
1.21 Either order:
   a. control growth
   b. change the food we eat into
     living matter
1.22 d
1.23 c
1.24 a
1.25 e
1.26

cell membrane
cytoplasm
nucleus

1.27 the outside of the cell that
holds the cell together

1.28 thick fluid in the cell that
contains chemicals
1.29 the control center of the cell
1.30 to take in
1.31 to send out
1.32 several organs working together

SECTION TWO

2.1   cranium

2.2   scapula
2.3   ilium
2.4   femur
2.5   phalanges

2.6   h
2.7   g
2.8   j
2.9   f

2.10   k
2.11   c

2.12   b
2.13   d
2.14   a
2.15   i
2.16   organs
2.17   206
2.18   muscles
2.19   marrow
2.20   b
2.21   c
2.22   a
2.23   b
2.24   c
2.25   true
2.26   true
2.27   false

2.28   Because cartilage is flexible.
        The ear is made of cartilage.
2.29   to make movement at the joints
        easier
2.30   skeleton
2.31   Any order:
        a. movement
        b. maintaining posture
        c. producing body heat
2.32   will
2.33   Any order:
        a. intestinal muscles
        b. stomach muscles
        c. blood vessel muscles
2.34   You control your voluntary muscles
        at will. The involuntary muscles
        are not controlled by will.
2.35   e
2.36   c
2.37   a
2.38   d
2.39   b
2.40   false
2.41   true
2.42   true
2.43   false
2.44   teacher check
2.45   epidermis
2.46   dermis
2.47   fatty layer
2.48   blood vessels
2.49   temperature

2.50 acne

2.51 Any order:
   a. epidermis
   b. dermis
   c. fatty layer

2.52 Albinos cannot manufacture melanin.

2.53 pigmentation, shield

SECTION THREE

3.1 axon

3.2 dendrite

3.3 brain (next nerve cell)

3.4 false

3.5 true

3.6 true

3.7 Example:
   The nerve cells in the tips of the
   fingers receive a stimulus and
   instantly send a message to the
   brain. A command to the muscles to
   pull the finger away is given by
   the brain. Your muscles contract
   and pull the finger away instantly.

3.8 brain stem

3.9 backbone

3.10 brain

3.11 axons

3.12 spinal cord

3.13 neuron

3.14 messages

3.15 false

3.16 true

3.17 true

3.18 false

3.19 the cerebrum

3.20 the cerebrum

3.21 the cerebellum

3.22 pupil large in dim light; small
   in bright light

3.23 Eye needs more light when room is dark.

3.24 cornea

3.25 pupil

3.26 iris

3.27 lens

3.28 retina

3.29 7

3.30 6

3.31 The student will find the lines are equal.

3.32 $\overline{AB}$

3.33 c

3.34 e

3.35 a

3.36 d

3.37 f

3.38 true

3.39 false

3.40 true

3.41 false

3.42 Any order:
   a. salty   c. sweet
   b. sour   d. bitter

3.43 false

3.44 true

3.45 true

3.46 false

3.47 Nerve endings in the back are farther apart.

3.48 c

3.49 d

3.50 b

3.51 a

SECTION ONE

1.1 Inspiration is breathing in
Expiration is breathing out.

1.2 Any order:

    a. sense of smell

    b. warms air

    c. cleans air

    or adds moisture, provides entrance for air

1.3 swells, mucus gets caught in nasal cavity, blocks passage of air

1.4 false

1.5 true

1.6 true

1.7 false

1.8 true

1.9 d

1.10 a

1.11 e

1.12 b

1.13 voice box

1.14 air

1.15 vocal cords

1.16 cartilage

1.17 false

1.18 true

1.19 true

1.20 true

1.21 g

1.22 b

1.23 d

1.24 e

1.25 a

1.26 c

1.27 mucous membrane

1.28 lungs

1.29 elastic

1.30 cilia

1.31 The easiest way to separate the slides is to slide them parallel to each other.

1.32 The two layers of pleura are separated by a thin layer of liquid just as the two layers of slides are separated by the water.

1.33 lobe

1.34 pleura

1.35 alveoli

1.36 heart

1.37 thorax

1.38 false

1.39 true

1.40 true

1.41 false

1.42 f

1.43 d

1.44 b

1.45 g

1.46 a

1.47　e

1.48　true

1.49　false

1.50　true

1.51　true

1.52　false

SECTION TWO

2.1　to the left of the center of the chest

2.2　pericardium

2.3　chambers

2.4　pulmonary artery

2.5　valves

2.6　auricles

2.7　false

2.8　true

2.9　false

2.10　true

2.11　teacher check

2.12　Teacher check – Your muscles gave off more carbon dioxide and needed more oxygen.

2.13　g

2.14　f

2.15　a

2.16　b

2.17　c

2.18　d

2.19　e

2.20　auricle

2.21　ventricle valve

2.22　ventricle

2.23　valves

2.24　The muscles and organs need more oxygen and food.

2.25　Arteries carry blood away from the heart.

2.26　The pulmonary artery carries blood only to the lungs. The aorta artery carries blood to the rest of the body.

2.27　organs

2.28　arterioles

2.29　heart

2.30　lungs

2.31　true

2.32　false

2.33　true

2.34　false

2.35　An artery is large and is the first tube the blood enters; a capillary is tiny and feeds the cells.

2.36　Capillaries carry blood from arteries to cells.

2.37　vein

2.38　heart

2.39　muscles

2.40　valves

2.41　true

2.42　false

2.43　false

2.44　true

2.45　a

2.46	e		2.62	pus
2.47	b		2.63	white blood cells
2.48	c		2.64	b
2.49	d		2.65	e
2.50	f		2.66	c
2.51	false		2.67	a
2.52	true		2.68	d
2.53	true		2.69	false
2.54	false		2.70	true
2.55	hemoglobin		2.71	true
2.56	oxygen		2.72	true
2.57	bone marrow		2.73	false
2.58	plasma		2.74	true
2.59	They defend the body against bacteria and disease.		2.75	true
			2.76	false
2.60	It makes blood cells.		2.77	teacher check
2.61	bacteria			

SECTION THREE

			3.11-3.12	Either order:
3.1	false		3.11	a. easier to chew and swallow food
3.2	true			
3.3	false		3.12	b. keeps mouth moist
3.4	true		3.13	false
3.5	e		3.14	true
3.6	d		3.15	true
3.7	a		3.16	false
3.8	c		3.17	e
3.9	becomes sweet		3.18	f
3.10	It has changed to sugar.		3.19	a

3.20	c		3.40	f
3.21	d		3.41	e
3.22	b		3.42	g
3.23	g		3.43	b
3.24	muscles		3.44	c
3.25	stomach		3.45	a
3.26	food		3.46	i
3.27	lungs		3.47	true
3.28	true		3.48	false
3.29	false		3.49	false
3.30	true		3.50	true
3.31	false		3.51	large intestine
3.32	starts digestion of protein		3.52	semisolid
3.33	breaks down protein, kills bacteria, changes sugar, helps make pepsin		3.53	digestion
			3.54	villi
3.34	Any order:		3.55	bloodstream

3.34 Any order:
   a. pancreas
   b. liver
   c. gall bladder

3.35 small intestine
3.36 villi
3.37 mucus

3.38 insulin

3.39 h

3.56 Any order:
   a. protein
   b. fat
   c. sugar
   d. starch
3.57 Any order:
   a. undigested fiber
   b. fat
   c. bacteria

SECTION FOUR

4.1	aorta		4.6	false
4.2	medulla		4.7	true
4.3	pelvis		4.8	true
4.4	nerves		4.9	d
4.5	true		4.10	b

4.11   e

4.12   a

4.13   20 percent

4.14   medulla

4.15   Any order:

    a. water

    b. sugar

    c. salt

4.16   false

4.17   true

4.18   false

4.19   true

4.20   true

4.21   perspiration

4.22   Either order:

    a. water

    b. salt

    c. other wastes

4.23   sweat glands

4.24   dermis

SECTION FIVE

5.1   made of elements or simple substances

5.2   a substance secreted by the body to regulate the body's chemical processes

5.3   work properly

5.4   make or produce

5.5   watch over, look out for

5.6   growth

5.7   glands

5.8   brain

5.9   Either order:

    a. anterior

    b. posterior

5.10   b

5.11   e

5.12   a

5.13   c

5.14   d

5.15   false

5.16   true

5.17   true

5.18   false

5.19   stress

5.20   two

5.21   triangular

5.22   moon-shaped

5.23   two

5.24   regulates the amount of potassium and sodium in the body

5.25   secretes hormones during stress that increase heartbeats

SECTION ONE

1.1   records
1.2   stating the problem
1.3   writing
1.4   unexplained
1.5   teacher check
1.6   true
1.7   true
1.8   false
1.9   false
1.10   teacher check
1.11   yes

1.12

DARK RED SPOTS

1.13   experiment
1.14   research
1.15   data
1.16   conclusion
1.17   hypothesis
1.18   a. stating the problem
       b. forming the hypothesis
       c. conducting an experiment
       d. interpreting data
       e. drawing conclusions
1.19   d
1.20   g
1.21   j

1.22   h
1.23   b
1.24   a
1.25   e
1.26   c
1.27   f
1.28   i
1.29   14.5 cm
1.30   measure of the amount of matter
1.31   amount of space that matter takes up
1.32   system of measurement used by scientists
1.33   meter
1.34   milli-
1.35   centimeter
1.36   milliliter
1.37   centigram
1.38   kilogram
1.39   teacher check
1.40   teacher check
1.41   teacher check
1.42   teacher check
1.43   geocentric
1.44   earth

1.45	epicycles	1.58	human body
1.46	5	1.59	freezing
1.47	circle	1.60	boiling
1.48	true	1.61	true
1.49	false	1.62	false
1.50	true	1.63	false
1.51	false	1.64	true
1.52	Any order:	1.65	i

1.52 Any order:
   a. Every object pulls at every other object.
   b. The amount of gravity depends on mass.
   c. The force of gravity between two objects depends on distance.

1.66	j		
1.67	a		
1.68	b		
1.53	e	1.69	h
1.54	d	1.70	c
1.55	a	1.71	d
1.56	b	1.72	k
1.57	Either order:	1.73	f
	a. ice	1.74	g
	b. salt		

SECTION TWO

2.1	constellations	2.10	true
2.2	myth	2.11	e
2.3	Polaris	2.12	c
2.4	Sirius	2.13	d
2.5	Ursa Major	2.14	b
2.6	Any order:	2.15	teacher check

2.6 Any order:
   a. heat
   b. size
   c. distance from the earth

		2.16	true
		2.17	false
2.7	true	2.18	true
2.8	false	2.19	true
2.9	true		

2.20   false

2.21   b

2.22   e

2.23   a

2.24   c

2.25   a. Mercury
        b. Venus
        c. Earth
        d. Mars

2.26   a. Jupiter
        b. Saturn
        c. Uranus
        d. Neptune

2.27   eight

2.28   Mercury

2.29   Venus

2.30   red

2.31   life

2.32   true

2.33   false

2.34   true

2.35   false

2.36   true

2.37   b

2.38   g

2.39   i

2.40   a

2.41   e

2.42   h

2.43   f

2.44   d

2.45   a. Mercury
        b. Venus
        c. Earth
        d. Mars
        e. asteroids
        f. Jupiter
        g. Saturn
        h. Uranus
        i. Neptune

2.46   planet

2.47   Either order:
        a. Mars
        b. Jupiter

2.48   Either order:
        a. gases
        b. dust

2.49   tail

2.50   d

2.51   e

2.52   b

2.53   a

2.54   a. last quarter
        b. new
        c. first quarter
        d. full

2.55   true

2.56   false

2.57   true

2.58   true

2.59   false

2.60   Any order:
        a. telescope
        b. spectroscope
        c. radio telescope
        d. spacecraft
        or camera

2.61   point in sky directly overhead

2.62   point in sky directly below
        observer

2.63 line where earth and sky seem to meet

2.64 points on celestial sphere directly above North and South poles

SECTION THREE

3.1 e

3.2 h

3.3 j

3.4 f

3.5 a

3.6 b

3.7 i

3.8 c

3.9 d

3.10 Examples; either order:
   a. particles – smoke and soot
   b. gasses – carbon monoxide and nitrogen oxide

3.11 Hydrocarbon gasses combine with nitrogen oxide, smoke, and soot.

3.12 a-d Examples:
   tune my car, burn no trash

3.13 teacher check

3.14 d

3.15 f

3.16 e

3.17 b

3.18 a

3.19 true

3.20 true

3.21 false

3.22 true

3.23 dew point

3.24 humidity

3.25 freezing

3.26 dew

3.27 Any order:
   a. cP
   b. mP
   c. cT
   d. mT

3.28 Any order:
   a. cirrus
   b. stratus
   c. cumulus

3.29 nimbostratus

3.30 cumulonimbus

3.31 upper troposphere

3.32 ice crystals

3.33 fog

3.34 thunderstorm

3.35 anvil

3.36 rain

3.37 warning

3.38 eye

3.39 watch

3.40 land *or* colder water

3.41 wispy, thin

3.42 layers of sheets

3.43 puffy, large

3.44 thunder, lightning, heavy rain, wind, sometimes hail; anvil-shaped clouds

3.45 rotating spiral, formed at the base of a cumulonimbus

3.46 thick clouds spiraling around a center of low pressure, called the eye; 200 to 400 miles in diameter; forms over warm oceans

3.47 cold air rushing out of a dying thunderstorm

3.48 Rain falls for 1 or 2 days, and then the weather becomes stable again.

3.49 The difference of temperatures prevents their air from mixing.

3.50 A cold front is formed when cold air pushes warm air. Heavy rains fall on both sides of the front.

3.51 An occluded front is when a fast-moving cold front meets a slow-moving cold front. The weather produced is rain, followed by clear skies, followed by more rain.

3.52 A stationary front is formed when a front stops moving. Produces weather similar to a warm front.

3.53 the boundary between two air masses

3.54 Warm air pushing against colder air moves over the cold front.

3.55 teacher check

3.56 Any order:
a. gather weather data
b. record the data
c. make predictions based upon the recorded data

3.57 Any order:
a. Weather stations observe the weather and record data.
b. Pilots radio in weather conditions.
c. Ships radio in weather conditions.
d. weather balloons
e. weather satellites

3.58 symbols

3.59 heat sensitive

3.60 code

3.61 masses

3.62 Any order:
a. temperature
b. air pressure
c. winds
d. precipitation

3.63 Any order:
a. Polar easterlies – 90° N
b. Prevailing westerlies 60° – 30° N
c. Northeast trades 30° N – 0°

3.64 Any order:
a. Southeast trades 0° – 30° S
b. Prevailing westerlies 30° – 60° S
c. Polar easterlies – 90° S

3.65 latitudes

3.66 low

3.67 east

3.68 Coriolis force

3.69 Any order:
a. latitude
b. altitude
c. nearness to water
d. average temperatures
e. average rainfall
f. ocean currents

3.70 Any order:
a. humid
b. arid
c. semiarid

3.71 North Atlantic Drift

3.72 The temperature of land is more influenced by sunshine than is water.

3.73 climate

3.74 80 inches or 200 cm

3.75 65° F and 100° F (or) 18° C and 38° C

3.76 plains or grasslands north of the equator

3.77	60 inches		3.82	c
3.78	65°		3.83	true
3.79	b		3.84	true
3.80	d		3.85	false
3.81	a			

SECTION FOUR

4.1	206		4.25	true
4.2	joint		4.26	Any order:
4.3	blood cells			a. intelligence
4.4	cartilage			b. will
4.5	calcium			c. memory
			4.27	Either order:
4.6	f			a. coordination
4.7	b			b. involuntary movements
4.8	d		4.28	e
4.9	a		4.29	b
4.10	c		4.30	a
4.11	e		4.31	d
			4.32	eye
4.12	false		4.33	taste buds or tongue
4.13	true		4.34	receptors
4.14	true		4.35	ear
4.15	false		4.36	nose
4.16	true			
			4.37	a. control activities of thyroid
4.17	temperature			b. growth rate and metabolism
4.18	contracting			c. deals with physical and
4.19	epidermis			emotional stress
4.20	fatty layer		4.38	hormones
4.21	false		4.39	brain
4.22	true		4.40	calcium
4.23	true		4.41	optical illusion
4.24	false		4.42	brain stem

4.43   d

4.44   b

4.45   c

4.46   a

4.47   e

4.48   breathing out

4.49   breathing in

4.50   d

4.51   b

4.52   c

4.53   a

4.54   f

4.55   true

4.56   false

4.57   true

4.58   true

4.59   e

4.60   a

4.61   d

4.62   b

4.63   Any order:
  a. red blood cells
  b. white blood cells
  c. platelets

4.64   Any order:
  a. type A
  b. type B
  c. type AB
  d. type O

4.65   arteries

4.66   veins

4.67   capillaries

4.68   platelets

4.69   plasma

4.70   pus

4.71   e

4.72   c

4.73   d

4.74   a

4.75   false

4.76   true

4.77   true

4.78   false

4.79   true

4.80   a. pancreas
  b. liver
  c. gall bladder

4.81   d

4.82   b

4.83   c

4.84   e

4.85   excretion

4.86   digestive

4.87   excretory

4.88   bladder

4.89   kidneys

4.90   Perspiration, a mixture of water, salt, and other wastes, is excreted through the sweat glands.

4.91   The outer shell removes 20 percent of the water and some salt, sugar, and waste products. Waste materials pass to the bladder.

4.92   "And the Lord God formed man of the dust of the ground, and breathed into his nostrils the breath of life; and man became a living soul."

Notes

SELF TEST 1

1.01 b

1.02 g

1.03 e

1.04 a

1.05 c

1.06 f

1.07 Any order:
   a. sight
   b. hearing
   c. taste
   d. smell
   e. feel (touch)

1.08 a

1.09 d

1.010 b

1.011 c

1.012 a

1.013 a

1.014 d

1.015 Any order:
   a. lion
   b. horse
   c. (canary) elephant
   d. lizard
   e. (eagle) mouse
   f. giraffe
   g. rattlesnake

1.016 Any order:
   a. canary
   b. rattlesnake
   c. alligator
   d. elephant

1.017 a

1.018 b

1.019 b. Some football players are good students.

1.020 a. All mothers see their babies as beautiful.

1.021 Hint:
Through careful observation man can learn much about many things. Write of some of the useful things man learns through observing.

SELF TEST 2

2.01 a. Stating the problem
   b. Forming the hypothesis
   c. Devising an experiment
   d. Interpreting data or observation
   e. Drawing conclusion

2.02 Examples:
   a. History of the area gathered from newspapers
   b. Colleagues or other knowledgeable people
   c. Professional publications

2.03 evening

2.04 calm

2.05 flat

2.06 No

2.07 white; From the North Pole, all directions are south; and polar bears live near the North Pole.

2.08 a. inquisitiveness

2.09 b. is about 150 words a minute

2.010 b. moisture and dust are important for rain

SELF TEST 3

3.01-3.04 Any order
3.01 astronomy
3.02 geology
3.03 chemistry
3.04 physics
3.05-3.08 Any order
3.05 botany
3.06 ecology
3.07 zoology

3.08 paleontology
3.09-3.014 Any order:

3.09 geography

3.010 psychology

3.011 economics
3.012 philosophy

3.013 anthropology

3.014 sociology

3.015 i

3.016 a

3.017 c

3.018 b

3.019 f

3.020 j

3.021 k

3.022 n

3.023 g
3.024 l
3.025 m
3.026 h
3.027 d
3.028 e
3.029 Hint; ideas to be included:
   a. Childhood – poor, slave, during Civil War, freed, frail, observed plants
   b. Education – hardship, poor, eager, worked his way, Master's degree
   c. Occupation – teacher, researcher, scientist of plants, greenhouse-keeper, laundryman
   d. Experiments – peanut, sweet potato, a variety of products (list three), 300 or 400 products
   e. Reliance on God – learned prayer early and prayed daily, learned from God the potential in plants, gave honor to God

3.030 ACROSS
   5. environment
   7. atom
   8. culture
   9. energy
   10. weather
   DOWN
   1. valid
   2. elements
   3. molecule
   4. atmosphere
   5. earthquake
   6. gravity

SELF TEST 4

4.01 e
4.02 c
4.03 b
4.04 g
4.05 d

4.06 a
4.07 i
4.08 f
4.09 j
4.010 l

4.011 k

4.012 theoretical

4.013 experimental

4.014 applied

4.015 chemists

4.016 Examples:
    1. All scientists are engaged in making scientific observations.
    2. They have a definite question in mind and are looking for specific information to answer that question.
    3. They have a passionate devotion to investigation and discovery.

4.017 The things man invents should help him have a better life rather than hurting him (example: gunpowder used in war is harmful).

4.018 A. Stating the problem
    B. Forming a hypothesis
    C. Searching for information
    D. Interpreting data
    E. Drawing conclusions

4.019 A. Any order:
      1. Astronomy
      2. Chemistry
      3. Geology
      4. Physics
    B. Any order:
      1. Botany
      2. Ecology
      3. Zoology
    C. Any order:
      1. Anthropology
      2. Economics
      3. Geography
      4. Psychology
      5. Sociology
    D. 1. Process of counting
      2. Process of thinking

4.020 A. 1. a. Theoretical
          b. Experimental
      2. Engineer
      3. Technician
      4. Teacher
    B. 1. a. Teaching
          b. Government agencies
          c. Industrial research
      2. a. Medicine
          b. Dentistry

SELF TEST 1

1.01 Any order:
    a. length
    b. temperature
    c. time
    d. mass

1.02 a. area
    b. volume (space)

1.03 a. France
    b. 1670

1.04 kilogram

1.05 meter

1.06 liter

1.07 cubit

1.08 Jesus Christ

1.09 true

1.010 false
    ~~mass~~; weight

1.011 true

1.012 false
    ~~weight~~; mass

1.013 true

1.014 true

1.015 true

1.016 d, m

1.017 c, L

1.018 b, cm^2

1.019 c, cm^3

1.020 a, g

1.021 d, cm

1.022 b, m^2

1.023 b, km^2

1.024 d, mm

1.025 c, ml

1.026 c, m^3

1.027 d, km

1.028 a, kg

1.029 a. 2 cm
    b. 5 cm
    c. 3 cm

1.030 a. 10 cm^2
    b. 6 cm^2
    c. 15 cm^2

1.031 30 cm^3

1.032 Example:
I will use the gram as the unit.
Place the shoe on one end of
the balance. I will add gram
masses to the other end until
it is balanced. I will count
the number of units used.

1.033 A cube 1 cm x 1 cm x 1 cm was
filled with water at 4 C. The
mass of the water was defined
as one gram.

1.034 Any order:
    a. based on the decimal system
    b. uses standard prefixes
    c. has only one unit for length,
       one for mass, one for volume,
       and so on.
    d. makes calculations easy

1.035 If the units are not standard,
we cannot understand the
measurements others make.

SELF TEST 2

2.01 true

2.02 false, ~~not~~

2.03 false, ~~circle~~; line

2.04 true

2.05   true
2.06   true
2.07   true
2.08   false, ~~not~~
2.09   true
2.010 true
2.011 true
2.012 true
2.013 false, ~~lines~~; symbols
2.014 true
2.015 true
2.016 false   ~~total~~   category
              ~~category~~   total

2.017 true
2.018 b
2.019 c

2.020 b
2.021 b
2.022 b, a
2.023 a, c, d
2.024 d or a
2.025 c, a, d
2.026 Checklist for a proper graph:

_____ 1. Title
_____ 2. Axis with arrows
_____ 3. Appropriate scale (most
            numbers divisible
            by 8-50 0,8,16…
            makes easy-to-use scale)
_____ 4. Accurate information
_____ 5. Appropriate graph (horizontal
            or vertical bar)

2.026 Example:

COMPARATIVE SPEEDS OF VARIOUS ANIMALS

Cheetah
Jack Rabbit
Gray Fox
Elephant
Ostrich
Man
Whale
Housefly
Trout
Snake

0   8   16   24   32   40   48   56   64   72   80   88   96   104   112
Speed (Kilometers per hour)

SELF TEST 1

1.01 four

1.02 equator

1.03 earth

1.04 Aristotle

1.05 planets

1.06 wanderers

1.07 meteoroids

1.08 meteors

1.09 meteorites

1.010 Any order:
a. the sun and stars – day and night
b. month; the motion of the moon
c. The stars marked the years and seasons.

1.011 Any order:
a. sun and moon across the sky
b. stars rise and set
c. sun's seasonal north-south progression

1.012 Any order:
a. rotation on its axis
b. revolution around the sun
c. solar system rotating on its axis
(or) galaxy moving away from other galaxies

1.013 Figure 6

1.014 Figure 7

1.015 a

1.016 e

1.017 h

1.018 c

1.019 l

1.020 d

1.021 f

1.022 i

1.023 b

1.024 j

1.025 k

1.026 They did not move as if they were fastened to spheres.

1.027 Any order:
a. Vega
b. Deneb
c. Altair

SELF TEST 2

2.01 Instrument: reflecting telescope
Operation: Light from moon reflects from large mirror, is bent by small 45° mirror, is focused at focal point, and is magnified by eyepiece.

2.02 Instrument: refracting telescope
Operation: Light from distant object comes through lens, is focused at focal point of objective lens, is magnified by eyepiece. Image is upside down.

2.03　Instrument:　radio telescope
　　　Operation:　Radio waves from
　　　space are gathered and
　　　reflected toward focal point
　　　where receiver receives; waves
　　　are transmitted to recording
　　　device.

2.04　size

2.05　40

2.06　Yerkes

2.07　light years

2.08　$186,000 \frac{mi.}{sec.}$

2.09　6 trillion

2.010　radio

2.011　cameras

2.012　spectroscope

2.013　closer

2.014　Either order:
　　　a.　moons of planets
　　　b.　Earth's moon

2.015　6

2.016　mirror

2.017　d

2.018　a

2.019　b

2.020　d

2.021　b

2.022　b

2.023　b

2.024　b

2.025　c

2.026　j

2.027　i

2.028　n

2.029　l

2.030　a

2.031　d

2.032　g

2.033　k

2.034　e

2.035　h

2.036　teacher check
　　　The sun is at one
　　　focus.　An ellipse
　　　describes the earth's
　　　path around sun.

2.037　When oriented to true
　　　north, full circle
　　　measures azimuth; half
　　　circle measures altitude
　　　above horizon.　Gives
　　　location of star.

2.038　The approach to mysteries
　　　changed from one of argument
　　　and reason to one of
　　　experiment and observation.

2.039　Polaris would be beneath
　　　your feet, with 8,000
　　　miles of earth in the way.

2.040　From the equator the horizon
　　　stretches from North Pole to
　　　South Pole.　All stars appear
　　　to rise and set, so some time
　　　during the year you could
　　　see each star.

SELF TEST 1

1.01   d
1.02   f
1.03   a
1.04   i
1.05   h
1.06   c
1.07   g
1.08   e
1.09   weather
1.010   coal
1.011   photosynthesis
1.012   oxygen
1.013   nuclear
1.014   Einstein

1.015   c
1.016   a
1.017   b
1.018   f
1.019   e
1.020   d
1.021   Example:
    a. proper temperature
    b. provides photosynthesis
    c. stored energy as coal, petroleum
    d. causes evaporation and precipitation
    e. heats some homes directly

SELF TEST 2

2.01   b
2.02   c
2.03   c
2.04   b or c
2.05   c

2.06   a

2.07   a

2.08   b

2.09   eight

2.010   counterclockwise
2.011   Pluto

2.012   Jupiter

2.013   Jovian (outer)

2.014   Venus
2.015   150,000,000

2.016   Saturn
2.017   away from

2.018   wanderers or *planetae*

2.019   rotation

2.020   day
2.021   elliptical
2.022   terrestrial or inner
2.023   sun
2.024   Photosynthesis is necessary for plants to produce food. This food is necessary to animal life either directly through eating plants or indirectly through eating animals that eat plants. Photosynthesis depends on light energy. We could not live without heat energy to warm Earth, create climate, and so forth.

2.025   A six-step reaction in which four hydrogen nuclei fuse to form one helium nucleus. The carbon atom is involved as a catalyst. Vast energy is released in the carbon cycle.
2.026   They are on the sun side of the earth.
2.027   They are on the daytime side of the earth. They are almost in a direct line between earth and sun and cannot be seen so close to the sun.

SELF TEST 3

3.01   kilometers

3.02   counterclockwise

3.03   Jovian or outer

3.04   Saturn

3.05   away from the sun

3.06 $29\frac{1}{2}$

3.07 $27\frac{1}{3}$

3.08 $29\frac{1}{2}$

3.09   a. moon
Either order:
b. sun
c. earth

3.010 wanderers or planetae

3.011 a. rotates
b. revolution

3.012 sun

3.013 6 hours 13 minutes

3.014 rotation

3.015 b

3.016 d

3.017 i

3.018 e

3.019 j

3.020 c

3.021 f

3.022 g

3.023 h

3.024 a

3.025 While the moon revolves around the earth for $27\frac{1}{3}$ days, the earth has moved along part of its curved path around the sun. The additional two-day journey of the moon brings it between the sun and the earth again. (See illustration on page 37.)

3.026 A wavy ellipse, with the sun at one focus of the ellipse.

4.01 $\frac{1}{2}$

4.02   full

4.03   new

4.04   lunar

4.05   solar

4.06   corona

4.07   hydrogen

4.08   Mercury

4.09   gravitation

4.010 counterclockwise

4.011 full

4.012 6 hours 13 minutes

SELF TEST 4

4.013 elliptical

4.014

4.015

4.016 The moon casts a small shadow.

4.017 b

4.018 a

4.019 c

4.020 d

4.021 c

SELF TEST 1

1.01	e	1.013	b
1.02	c	1.014	a
1.03	a	1.015	c
1.04	d	1.016	b
1.05	f	1.017	false
1.06	c	1.018	mesosphere
1.07	b	1.019	thermosphere
1.08	g	1.020	equals
1.09	a	1.021	The main factor that changes is the temperature.
1.010	c	1.022	The gases in the troposphere, stratosphere, and mesosphere are mixed uniformly.
1.011	b	1.023	The ozonosphere absorbs most of the ultraviolet rays that reach earth from the sun.
1.012	b		

SELF TEST 2

2.01	g	2.013	d
2.02	j	2.014	b
2.03	i	2.015	a
2.04	c	2.016	b
2.05	h	2.017	b
2.06	e	2.018	a
2.07	a	2.019	a
2.08	d	2.020	d
2.09	b	2.021	b
2.010	f	2.022	b
2.011	d	2.023	a
2.012	a	2.024	a

2.025 d
2.026 true
2.027 true
2.028 true
2.029 true

2.030 carbon dioxide and energy
2.031 energy and carbon dioxide
2.032 denitrification
2.033 legumes
2.034 plants or other animals

SELF TEST 3

3.01 n
3.02 l
3.03 c
3.04 m
3.05 o
3.06 a
3.07 j
3.08 e
3.09 g
3.010 k
3.011 i

3.012 f

3.013 b

3.014 h

3.015 b

3.016 a

3.017 c

3.018 a

3.019 a

3.020 d

3.021 b

3.022 a
3.023 b

3.024 d
3.025 b
3.026 a
3.027 a
3.028 b
3.029 a
3.030 c
3.031 c
3.032 b
3.033 b
3.034 b
3.035 true

3.036 false

3.037 true

3.038 true

3.039 true

3.040 stratosphere

3.041 denitrification

3.042 Either order:
    a. particles
    b. gases

3.043 ionosphere

3.044 Clean Air Act

SELF TEST 1

1.01	e	1.020	d
1.02	f	1.021	a
1.03	d	1.022	b
1.04	g	1.023	d
1.05	i	1.024	b
1.06	h	1.025	c
1.07	a	1.026	true
1.08	j	1.027	true
1.09	b	1.028	true
1.010	c	1.029	condensation nuclei
1.011	a	1.030	Any order:

1.030 Any order:
   a. rain
   b. snow
   c. sleet
   d. hail

1.031 Any order:
   a. temperature
   b. pressure
   c. wind
   d. moisture

1.012 d

1.013 a

1.014 d

1.015 a

1.016 c

1.032 A comparison of the actual amount of water vapor in the air to the maximum amount it can hold, expressed as a percent.

1.017 b

1.018 a

1.019 b

1.033 Air always moves from an area of high pressure to an area of low pressure.

SELF TEST 2

2.01	c	2.07	j
2.02	b	2.08	g
2.03	i	2.09	d
2.04	h	2.010	a
2.05	e	2.011	d
2.06	f	2.012	c

2.013 c

2.014 c

2.015 c

2.016 a

2.017 b

2.018 c

2.019 a

2.020 b

2.021 a

2.022 d

2.023 a

2.024 c

2.025 b

2.026 true

2.027 false

2.028 true

2.029 false

2.030 true

2.031 warm

2.032 temperature

2.033 thunderstorm

2.034 eye

2.035 occluded

2.036 A warm front is a front formed when warm air pushes colder air.

2.037 Air over the equator is becoming warm and rising.

2.038 An air mass is a large body of air that has uniform temperatures and humidity.

2.039 A tornado is a narrow, funnel-shaped cloud with rapidly rotating winds.

2.040 A hurricane is a large, revolving storm with destructive winds, heavy rains, and high waves.

SELF TEST 3

3.01 i

3.02 h

3.03 d

3.04 j

3.05 a

3.06 g

3.07 f

3.08 c

3.09 e

3.010 b

3.011 a

3.012 b

3.013 c

3.014 b

3.015 c

3.016 a

3.017 d

3.018 a

3.019 a

3.020 b

3.021 b

3.022 c

3.023 b

3.024 a

3.025 c or d
3.026 false

3.027 true

3.028 true
3.029 true

3.030 false
3.031 air pressure

3.032 temperature
3.033 west
3.034 warm

3.035 maritime tropical
3.036 The eye has few clouds, light or no winds, and no rain.
3.037 The Coriolis Effect is the tendency of moving objects to curve because of the earth's rotation.
3.038 These air masses are called maritime tropical and are warm and moist.
3.039 a rising barometer and winds between the southwest and northwest

3.040

SELF TEST 1

1.01	false		1.015	weather
1.02	false		1.016	climate
1.03	false		1.017	solar radiation
1.04	true		1.018	water
1.05	true		1.019	trade winds
1.06	true		1.020	a. west
1.07	true			b. east
1.08	true		1.021	polar easterlies
1.09	true		1.022	prevailing westerlies
1.010	false		1.023	northeast trade winds
1.011	14.7 lbs. per sq. inch		1.024	southeast trade winds
1.012	hail (or hailstones)		1.025	prevailing westerlies
1.013	rotates		1.026	polar easterlies
1.014	equator			

SELF TEST 2

2.01	true		2.012	most
2.02	true		2.013	cold
2.03	true		2.014	lower
2.04	false		2.015	humidity (rainfall or heat)
2.05	false		2.016	breeze
2.06	true		2.017	maritime
2.07	false			
2.08	true			
2.09	true			
2.010	true			
2.011	Example:			

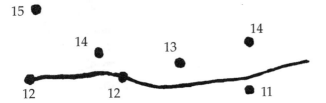

2.018 equator
2.019 horse latitudes
2.020 equator
2.021 Labrador Current

2.022 isotherms
2.023 west
2.024 axis

SELF TEST 3

3.01 d
3.02 j
3.03 g

3.04 l
3.05 b
3.06 e
3.07 i
3.08 a
3.09 h
3.010 c
3.011 equator
3.012 savannas
3.013 climate

3.014 from which they blow
3.015 dry
3.016 Either order:
       a. North Pole
       b. South Pole
3.017 permafrost
3.018 Antarctica
3.019 Gulf Stream
3.020 cold *or* polar
3.021 60° N
3.022 30° N
3.023 0°
3.024 30° S
3.025 60° S

SELF TEST 4

4.01 camel

4.02 wooden

4.03 oasis

4.04 market

4.05 Pygmies

4.06 Bedouins

4.07 thatched

4.08 seals

4.09 poisoned

4.010 winter

4.011
4.012
4.013
4.014
4.015
4.016

4.017 tropical rain forest

4.018 tropical savanna

4.019 the Gulf Stream

4.020 because of permafrost

4.021 desert (arid)

4.022 trading

4.023 hunting and gathering

4.024 answer will fit community where project is completed

4.025 Any of these: furs, fish, seals, caribou

4.026 farming

SELF TEST 1

1.01   c

1.02   a

1.03   b

1.04   c

1.05   b

1.06   a

1.07   c

1.08   b

1.09   a

1.010 c

1.011 d

1.012 i

1.013 h

1.014 b

1.015 g

1.016 a

1.017 f

1.018 e

1.019 cells

1.020 cell membrane

1.021 nucleus

1.022 excretion

1.023 DNA

1.024 liquid

1.025 system

1.026 true

1.027 true

1.028 false

1.029 true

1.030 false

1.031 true

1.032 true

1.033 false

1.034 Absorption means to take in and excretion means to send out.

1.035 Refer to procedure in LIFEPAC following Activity 1.5.

1.036

cell membrane
cytoplasm
nucleus

1.037 cells

1.038 tissues

1.039 organs

SELF TEST 2

2.01 skin

2.02 voluntary muscles

2.03 joint

2.04 tissues

2.05 nucleus

2.06

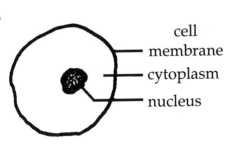

2.07 a. compact bone

b. marrow

2.08 d

2.09 e

2.010 h

2.011 b

2.012 k

2.013 f

2.014 a

2.015 c

2.016 g

2.017 j

2.018 false

2.019 true

2.020 true

2.021 false

2.022 true

2.023 d

2.024 b

2.025 a

2.026 c

2.027 d

SELF TEST 3

3.01 d

3.02 e

3.03 h

3.04 g

3.05 j

3.06 a

3.07 f

3.08 k

3.09 m

3.010 b

3.011 l

3.012 i

3.013 false

3.014 true

3.015 true

3.016 true

3.017 c

3.018 c

3.019 Any order:
  a. smell
  b. hearing
  c. touch
  d. sight
  e. taste

3.020 Any order:
  a. epidermis
  b. dermis
  c. fatty layer

3.021 Any order:
  a. salty
  b. sweet
  c. bitter
  d. sour

3.022 a. I
  b. I
  c. V
  d. I
  e. V
  f. V
  g. V

3.023 a. cerebrum
  b. cerebrum
  c. cerebellum
  d. cerebrum
  e. cerebellum
  f. cerebrum
  g. cerebrum

SELF TEST 1

1.01   i

1.02   h

1.03   d

1.04   b

1.05   c

1.06   g

1.07   a

1.08   e

1.09   c

1.010 b

1.011 d

1.012 a

1.013 b

1.014 c

1.015 d

1.016 inspiration is breathing in;
       expiration is breathing out

1.017 Either order:
       a. sense of smell
       b. cleans air on its way to lungs

1.018 Lungs take in oxygen from the
       air; the heart pumps blood to
       carry oxygen to the body and
       to carry carbon dioxide back
       to the lungs from the body;
       lungs exhale carbon dioxide.

SELF TEST 2

2.01   veins

2.02   pericardium

2.03   ventricles

2.04   arteries or ventricle valves

2.05   septum

2.06   Any order:
       a. smell
       b. cleans air
       c. carries air to the lungs

2.07   Any order:
       a. red blood cells
       b. white blood cells
       c. platelets

2.08   carry oxygen to the cells and
       return carbon dioxide and other
       wastes to lungs from the cells

2.09   fight infection by killing
       bacteria

2.010 cluster, or group, together to
       help stop bleeding

2.011

Right Side   Left Side

2.012 arteries carry blood away from
       the heart; veins carry blood to
       the heart

2.013 Lungs get oxygen from air and heart pumps it via red blood cells to every cell in the body.

2.014 true

2.015 false

2.016 true

2.017 false

2.018 true

SELF TEST 3

3.01 b

3.02 a

3.03 e

3.04 f

3.05 c

3.06 d

3.07 g

3.08 k

3.09 h

3.010 i

3.011 Any order:

    a. receives and moves food

    b. breaks down and absorbs food

    c. a protector for the body

    d. a mirror of the emotions

3.012 Any order; Examples:

    a. passage to lungs

    b. cleans air

    c. sense of smell

3.013 Any order:

    a. red blood cells

    b. white blood cells

    c. platelets

3.014 projections in intestine that absorb food

3.015 chemical that breaks down food

3.016 substance that is made or produced

3.017 smallest particle of a substance without a chemical change

3.018 air sacs in lung

3.019 true

3.020 false

3.021 false

3.022 true

3.023 false

3.024 true

3.025 true

3.026 true

3.027 true

3.028 false

3.029 false

3.030 villi

3.031 pulp chamber

3.032 bacteria

3.033 esophagus

3.034 glands

3.035 pylorus

3.036 platelets

3.037 lungs

3.038 plasma

SELF TEST 4

4.01   true
4.02   true
4.03   true
4.04   false
4.05   true
4.06   true
4.07   false
4.08   false
4.09   true
4.010 g
4.011 f
4.012 b
4.013 d
4.014 e

4.015 a

4.016 b

4.017 a

4.018 c

4.019 d

4.020 a

4.021

Aorta

Pulmonary Artery

Valves

Auricles

Ventricles

Right Side   Left Side

4.022 The kidneys reclaim or reabsorb the water, sugar, and salt.
4.023 The enamel is dead and cannot regrow.
4.024 Red blood cells carry the oxygen from the lungs to the rest of the body.

4.025 When you swallow your trachea automatically closes. If food does go down your trachea you cough it up.

SELF TEST 5

5.01   b
5.02   c
5.03   d
5.04   e
5.05   a
5.06   h

5.07   g
5.08   monitors other glands; controls growth through thyroid; chemical supervisor of body
5.09   controls growth and metabolism
5.010 regulates amount of sodium and potassium in body; helps body deal with stress; secretes hormones to make heart beat faster

5.011 arteries take blood from heart; veins take blood to heart

5.012 expiration is breathing out; inspiration is breathing in

5.013 prevent body from losing too much water, sugar, or salt or to filter impurities from the blood

5.014 platelets

5.015 infection

5.016 cell

5.017 intestines

5.018 growth and other glands

5.019 pituitary gland

5.020 tiny projections in the intestines that absorb food

5.021 substance that causes changes in other substances

5.022 churning motion in digestive muscles

5.023 regulates the body's chemical processes

5.024 breathing in

5.025 breathing out

SELF TEST 1

1.01 f

1.02 b

1.03 d

1.04 a

1.05 e

1.06 i

1.07 h

1.08 g

1.09 true

1.010 false

1.011 true

1.012 false

1.013 true

1.014 true

1.015 false

1.016 true

1.017 b

1.018 c

1.019 d

1.020 a

1.021 c

1.022 b

1.023 a. state problem
 b. form hypothesis
 c. conduct experiment
 d. interpret data
 e. draw conclusions

1.024 Any order:
 a. line graph
 b. bar graph
 c. pictograph
 d. circle graph

SELF TEST 2

2.01 d

2.02 j

2.03 g

2.04 a

2.05 f

2.06 b

2.07 i

2.08 h

2.09 c

2.010 a

2.011 d

2.012 c

2.013 d

2.014 c

2.015 b

2.016 c

2.017 a

2.018 a. Mercury
 b. Venus
 c. Earth
 d. Mars
 e. asteroids
 f. Jupiter
 g. Saturn
 h. Uranus
 i. Neptune

2.019 a. last quarter
 b. new
 c. first quarter
 d. full

SELF TEST 3

3.01   g

3.02   f

3.03   b
3.04   e
3.05   a
3.06   c

3.07   d

3.08   j
3.09   h

3.010 k

3.011 Any order:
    a. temperature
    b. air pressure
    c. wind
    d. moisture
3.012 a. state problem
    b. form hypothesis
    c. conduct experiment
    d. interpret data
    e. draw conclusions
3.013 Any order:
    a. maritime
    b. polar
    c. tropical
    d. continental

3.014 Any order:
    a. stratus
    b. cirrus
    c. cumulus
3.015 Any order:
    a. gather weather data
    b. record the data
    c. make predictions based upon
       the recorded data
3.016 length
3.017 eye
3.018 barometer
3.019 mercury
3.020 temperature
3.021 star pattern
3.022 scientific or educated guess
3.023 a taking up
3.024 large area of high winds and
    thunderstorms
3.025 small, violent, short-lived storm
3.026 hot and wet region near the equator
3.027 dry
3.028 cP
3.029 mP
3.030 mT
3.031 cT

SELF TEST 4

4.01   h
4.02   g
4.03   f
4.04   e
4.05   c

4.06   a
4.07   i
4.08   j
4.09   d
4.010 b

4.011 a

4.012 d

4.013 d

4.014 b

4.015 b

4.016 d

4.017 a

4.018 a

4.019 c

4.020 Expiration is breathing out.
Inspiration is breathing in.

4.021 Absorption means to take in.
Excretion means to let out.

4.022 a. Mercury
b. Venus
c. Earth
d. Mars
e. Jupiter
f. Saturn
g. Uranus
h. Neptune

4.023 a. digestive
b. nervous
c. excretory
d. circulatory
e. nervous
f. digestive
g. respiratory
h. excretory
i. respiratory

Notes

Science 701
LIFEPAC Test

1. false
2. true
3. false
4. true
5. false
6. false
7. true
8. true
9. false
10. false
11. Any order:
    a. taste
    b. touch
    c. sight
    d. smell
    e. hearing
12. instruments
13. hypothesis
14. data
15. Either order
    a. peanuts
    b. sweet potatoes
16. Physical
17. Social
18. Biological
19. Mathematics
20. f
21. h
22. b
23. k
24. d
25. j

26. a
27. i
28. c
29. g
30. a. 2
    b. 3
    c. 1
    d. 3
    e. 2
    f. 3
    g. 3
    h. 1
    i. 1
    j. 2
    k. 2
    l. 1
31. deductive
32. inductive
33. a. Ecology is the study of relation-
       ship of plants and animals to
       their environment
    b. Science is systematically organized
       knowledge.
    Examples:
34. fur, small
35. four legs
36. pets, ears, mammals
    Examples:
37. offspring
38. trainability
39. sounds

Science 702
LIFEPAC Test

1. i
2. b
3. e
4. a
5. j
6. c
7. k
8. d
9. f
10. g
11. h
12. d
13. c
14. b
15. c
16. a
17. measurement
18. France
19. meter
20. mass
21. a. wisdom
    b. stature
    c. God
    d. man
22. graph
23. line
24. pictographs

25. circle
26. true
27. true
28. false
29. false
30. Any order, any three:
    a. based on decimal system
    b. uses same prefixes
    c. uses only one unit per category of measurement
    d. Computations are easier.
31. Use the cm unit.
    Find out how many cm units fit along the edge of your paper.
32. a. bar
    b. line
    c. pictograph
    d. circle
33. a. 3 cm
    b. 2 cm
    c. 4 cm
34. a. 12 cm^2
    b. 8 cm^2
    c. 6 cm^2
35. 24 cm^3

Science 703
LIFEPAC Test

1. a. orbits
    b. elliptical
2. rotation
3. day
4. Aristotle
5. sun
6. refracting
7. light
8. Galileo
9. light year
10. b
11. d
12. d
13. It helped man discover the nature of the heavenly bodies and their motions.
14. The larger the lens, the greater the magnification.
15. Because distances are so great it would be nearly impossible to work with such large numbers.
16. Aristotle did not experiment; he was interested in the *why*. Newton found experiments necessary to define the *what* and *how*.

17. a. First to use the telescope; "father of modern science"; found evidence for heliocentric theory
    b. First in modern times to promote the heliocentric theory
    c. Wrote laws of planetary motion
    d. Published the law of universal gravitation
    e. First to suggest that earth orbited sun
18. Any order:
    a. motion of sun and moon across sky
    b. motion against background of fixed stars
    c. seasonal motion north and south from horizon
19. geocentric: earth at center; heavenly bodies orbit earth. heliocentric; sun at center; bodies orbit sun.

Science 704
LIFEPAC Test

1.   g
2.   c
3.   i
4.   a
5.   l
6.   e
7.   h
8.   n
9.   d
10. b
11. p
12. o
13. k
14. q
15. m
16. j
17. f
18. coal
19. photosynthesis
20. fusion
21. temperature
22. weather
23. gravity
24. Either order:
     a. Mercury
     b. Earth
25. phases
26. 150,000,000 km
27. axis
28. Mars
29. Galileo
30. Saturn
31. Uranus
32. Neptune
33. a. Venus
     b. Neptune
34. Pluto
35. 1986
36. Jupiter
37. Either order:
     a. Mercury
     b. Venus
38. counterclockwise

39. east
40. 13°
41. later
42. a. 27 $\frac{1}{3}$
     b. 29 $\frac{1}{2}$
43. 29 $\frac{1}{2}$ days
44. a. Moon
     Either order:
     b. Earth
     c. Sun
45. straight line
46. solar eclipse
47. Earth   Moon

48.

     Moon   Earth
49. Examples:
     a. light
     b. photosynthesis
     c. heat
     d. fuel or weather
     or electricity and so forth
50. Any order: any five
     a. combustion
     b. contraction
     c. meteor impact
     d. radioactive substances
     e. carbon cycle
     f. proton-proton
51. a. Mercury
     b. Venus
     c. Earth
     d. Mars
     e. Jupiter
     f. Saturn
     g. Uranus
     h. Neptune

Science 705
LIFEPAC Test

1.	b
2.	d
3.	h
4.	i
5.	g
6.	c
7.	e
8.	j
9.	a
10.	f
11.	a
12.	c
13.	d
14.	b
15.	a
16.	d

17.	b
18.	a
19.	a
20.	c
21.	a
22.	a
23.	c
24.	equals
25.	plants or photosynthesis
26.	oxygen
27.	dominion
28.	golden rule
29.	false
30.	true
31.	true

Science 706
LIFEPAC Test

1.	d
2.	b
3.	c
4.	h
5.	e
6.	j
7.	f
8.	g
9.	a
10.	i
11.	b
12.	a
13.	d
14.	b
15.	b
16.	d
17.	a

18.	b
19.	a
20.	a
21.	d
22.	d
23.	a
24.	c
25.	c
26.	temperature
27.	dew point
28.	on both sides
29.	stationary
30.	maritime tropical
31.	true
32.	true
33.	false

Science 707
LIFEPAC Test

1. true
2. true
3. true
4. false
5. true
6. true
7. false
8. false
9. false
10. true
11. i
12. k
13. h
14. j
15. a

16. c
17. e
18. b
19. d
20. g
21. c. fur trading
22. a. poisoned arrows
23. a. farming
24. c. Labrador Current
25. a. very warm
26. b. hail
27. a. dry
28. a. 0°
29. c. the Sahara Desert
30. c. meteorologists

Science 708
LIFEPAC Test

1. true
2. false
3. false
4. true
5. true
6. h
7. g
8. f
9. j
10. c
11. a
12. b
13. e
14. d
15. d
16. c

17. a
18. b
19. b
20. the first 3" of the spinal cord
21. to take in
22. the main pathway for all of the body's messages
23. to make clear
24. Any order:
   a. touch
   b. taste
   c. sight
   d. hearing
   e. smell

Science 709
LIFEPAC Test

1. true
2. true
3. false
4. true
5. d
6. a
7. b
8. c
9. e
10. f
11. j
12. g
13. h
14. i
15. k
16. l
17. excretory
18. respiratory
19. circulatory
20. endocrine
21. digestive

22. digestive
23. circulatory
24. excretory
25. respiratory
26. endocrine
27. endocrine
28. circulatory
29. digestive
30. excretory
31. Any order:
    a. red blood cells
    b. white blood cells
    c. platelets
32. d
33. c
34. c
35. b
36. b
37. a
38. d

Science 710
LIFEPAC Test

1. f
2. e
3. a
4. b
5. k
6. j
7. c
8. d
9. h
10. g
11. a
12. b
13. a
14. c
15. d
16. b
17. d
18. d
19. a

20. b
21. true
22. true
23. false
24. true
25. experiment
26. counterclockwise direction
27. brain
28. polar easterlies
29. a. Mercury
    b. Venus
    c. Earth
    d. Mars
    e. asteroids
    f. Jupiter
    g. Saturn
    h. Uranus
    i. Neptune

1. true
2. true
3. true
4. false
5. false
6. false
7. true
8. true
9. false
10. true
11. senses
12. conclusion
13. hypothesis
14. physical science
15. living organisms
16. science
17. ecology
18. botany
19. George Washington Carver
20. g
21. b
22. e
23. h
24. a
25. d
26. j
27. c
28. i
29. f

30.
  a. 3
  b. 1
  c. 2
  d. 1
  e. 2
  f. 3
  g. 1
  h. 1
  i. 2
  j. 1
  k. 3
  l. 2
31. deductive
32. deductive
33.
  a. A systematic grouping of items or objects using distinguishing properties of the items to subdivide the total group into small classes with similar properties.
  b. An idea based upon facts to best explain a situation or phenomenon.

34. Examples:
  a. hair
  b. four legs
  c. pets, mammals, or etc.

35. Examples:
  a. sounds
  b. feet
  c. teeth

1. g
2. j
3. k
4. a
5. h
6. f
7. i
8. c
9. b
10. d
11. e
12. a
13. b
14. c
15. d
16. b
17. metric system
18. length
19. gravity
20. weight
21. standard unit
22. graphs

23. mass
24. bar graphs
25. vertical
26. true
27. false
28. true
29. true
30. Any order:
    a. line
    b. bar
    c. circle
    d. pictograph
31. a. 1 cm
    b. 1.4 cm = 1 cm
    c. 3 cm
    d. 2.7 cm = 3 cm
    e. 3 cm
32. bar
33. three days
34. 32°C
35. 7.7 or 7.8 days

1. j
2. e
3. c
4. f
5. g
6. b
7. i
8. a
9. h
10. revolution
11. reflecting
12. ellipses
13. astrolabe
14. altitude
15. meteor
16. spectroscope
17. Any order:
    a. planets travel in elliptical orbits
    b. the speed of a planet moving around the sun changes all the time
    c. the period of a planet's revolution is related to the planet's distance from the sun
18. The earth is in action, but the earth's rotation and revolution seem to make the heavenly bodies move as we observe them.

19. see drawings at right

20. Example:
    a cow tied to a post, the cow is the earth, the post is the sun, and the rope is gravity
21. Any order:
    a. position of moon changes from night to night
    b. sun is eclipsed and moon is eclipsed
    c. planets do not move like stars do
22. Either order:
    a. wanderers do not always move eastward against the background of the stars
    b. sometimes they seem to be closer, larger, and brighter than at other times

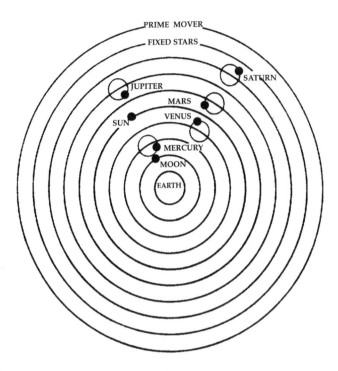

geocentric theory

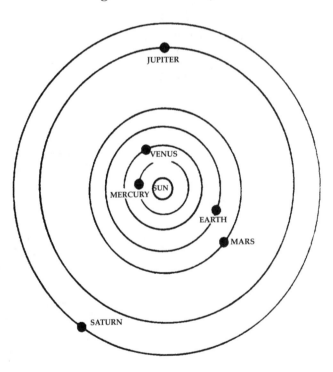

heliocentric theory

1. false
2. true
3. true
4. false
5. true
6. true
7. false
8. false
9. true
10. false
11. f
12. c
13. k
14. j
15. i
16. h
17. b
18. a
19. d
20. g
21. eclipse or solar eclipse
22. a. Venus
    b. Neptune
23. Either order:
    a. Mercury
    b. Venus

24. Either order:
    a. Venus
    b. Mars
25. later
26. nuclear reaction or fusion or carbon cycle
27. temperature
28. east
29. a. rotates
    b. revolution
30. nine
31. a. Mercury
    b. Venus
    c. Earth
    d. Mars
    e. Jupiter
    f. Saturn
    g. Uranus
    h. Neptune
32. Any order, any five:
    a. combustion
    b. contraction
    c. meteor-impact
    d. radioactive substances
    e. carbon cycle
    f. proton-proton

33.

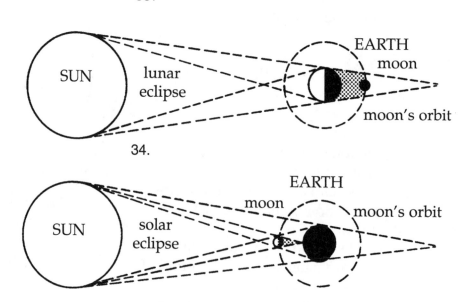

34.

1. f
2. k
3. j
4. i
5. a
6. c
7. b
8. g
9. h
10. d
11. golden rule
12. Either order:
    a. particles
    b. gases
13. nitrogen
14. temperature
15. carbon dioxide
16. burning fossil fuels
17. Either order:
    a. respiration
    b. photosynthesis
18. oceans
19. c
20. b
21. a
22. a
23. b
24. false
25. false

26. true
27. false
28. true
29. true
30. true

1. f

2. a

3. e

4. i

5. g

6. j

7. h

8. c

9. d

10. b

11. b

12. d

13. a

14. d

15. a

16. c

17. a

18. b

19. c

20. d

21. true

22. true

23. false

24. false

25. true

26. dew point

27. continental polar

28. Coriolis effect

29. warm

30. waterspouts

31. Any four:
    a. weather stations
    b. airplanes
    c. weather balloons
    d. foreign countries or ships, satellites

32. Any order:
    a. cirrus
    b. stratus
    c. cumulus

1. i

2. h

3. c

4. g

5. e

6. a

7. b

8. k

9. j

10. d

11. a

12. c

13. c

14. b

15. a

16. b

17. a

18. a

19. b

20. b

21. true

22. false

23. false

24. false

25. true

26. true

27. true

28. false

29. true

30. true

31. Any order:
    a. temperature
    b. pressure
    c. wind
    d. precipitation

32. teacher check:
    The students' responses
    will depend on their
    geographical location.

1. false
2. false
3. true
4. true
5. false
6. true
7. false
8. true
9. true
10. false
11. Any order:
    a. salty
    b. sour
    c. sweet
    d. bitter
12. cell theory
13. Any order:
    a. dermis
    b. epidermis
    c. fatty layer
14. cartilage
15. pupil
16. stimulus
17. Either order:
    a. axons
    b. dendrites
18. b
19. e
20. f
21. a
22. c
23.

24. Any order:
    a. sight
    b. hearing
    c. taste
    d. touch
    e. smell
25.

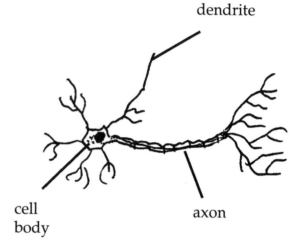

cell
body   axon   dendrite

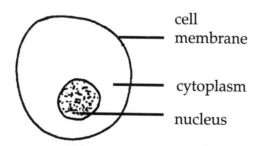

cell
membrane

cytoplasm

nucleus

1. b

2. h

3. k

4. f

5. a

6. i

7. j

8. c

9. e

10. g

11. false

12. false

13. false

14. true

15. false

16. false

17. true

18. true

19. false

20. true

21. pelvis

22. valves

23. septum

24. arteries

25. villi

26. lungs

27. Either order:
   a. anterior
   b. posterior

28. cell

29. circulatory

30. excretory

31. digestive

32. circulatory

33. endocrine

34. Any order:
   a. white blood cells
   b. red blood cells
   c. platelets

35. Example:
   When you swallow food your windpipe (trachea) automatically closes.

1. h
2. k
3. i
4. j
5. g
6. b
7. a
8. d
9. e
10. c
11. respiration
12. Either order:
    a. Mars
    b. Jupiter
13. sunlight
14. mT
15. dew point
16. true
17. false
18. true
19. false
20. true
21. true
22. false
23. true
24. false
25. true
26. d
27. b
28. d
29. c
30. a
31. d
32. Any order:
    a. continental
    b. maritime
    c. polar
    d. tropical
33. Any order:
    a. red blood cells
    b. white blood cells
    c. platelets